The Last of the Mohicans

by

James Fenimore Cooper

Simple English Classics Series

Adapted by
Elizabeth V. DiSomma
and
Mary Louise McTiernan

Illustrated by Anita Jones

Dormac, Inc.

Simple English Classics Series

Acknowledgement

Pronunciation key and diacritical marks are from *Scott, Foresman Advanced Dictionary* by Thorndike/Barnhart. Copyright © 1983 by Scott, Foresman and Company. Reprinted by permission.

© Dormac, Incorporated 1987

First Printing 1987
Second Printing 1988

DORMAC, INC.
P.O. Box 270459
San Diego, CA 92128-0983

ISBN 0-86575-592-2

Printed in U.S.A.

The Last of the Mohicans

Table of Contents

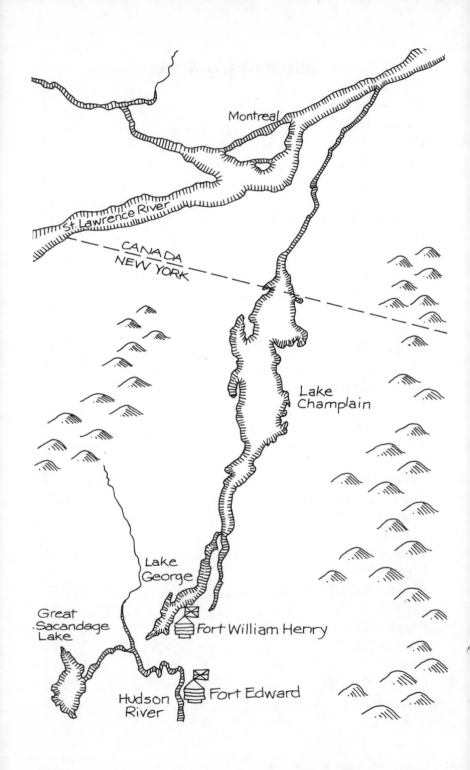

The Last of the Mohicans

Chapter I

During the colonial wars of North America, a wilderness separated the possessions of the two enemies, France and England. The soldiers of both armies often spent months in the rough forests, seeking their enemies. The country between the upper Hudson River and the nearby lakes experienced the cruelty of the fierce warfare of that time.

Lake Champlain stretched from Canada into New York and formed a natural way across half the distance the French had to travel to battle their enemies. Near Champlain's southern end was another lake, called by the French *du Saint Sacrement*, and by the English *Lake George*. Both countries ignored the early native name of *Horican*.

Most of the battles for the control of the colonies were fought in this area. The two armies built forts at different points along the route, took and retook them, destroyed and rebuilt them.

Our story occurred during the last war which England and France fought for a country that neither would be able to hold.

Toward the end of a day in midsummer, an Indian runner brought news to Fort Edward that the French general, Montcalm, was moving up the Champlain with a large army. The runner also carried an important message from Munro, the commander of Fort William Henry, for speedy and powerful help. Munro held the fort with a force too small to fight against Montcalm. At Fort Edward, General Webb received the message. He commanded the armies of the king in the northern territory, with more than five thousand men.

News spread through the camp that a force of fifteen hundred men would depart at daybreak for Fort William Henry to the north. Soon a selected group received orders to prepare for speedy departure, and all made the necessary preparations.

As the following day began to brighten the sky, the whole camp awoke. The chosen group was soon ready to leave. The trained soldiers of the king marched to the right of the line, and the colonists took their positions on its left. The soldiers, scouts, and strongly guarded supply wagons had all left the camp before the gray morning saw the sun.

There remained signs of another departure. Before the log cabin of the English general were several horses. The decorations on two of the horses showed they would carry females of high position, which was unusual in that wild country. A third wore the equipment of an officer, while *the rest** were for servants who were already waiting. At a respectful distance, groups of curious people watched the preparations.

There was one man who was unusual. This person was tall, with long arms, a long, thin neck, and longer and thinner legs. A large hat topped his head. He walked into the center of the servants, freely expressing his thoughts about the horses.

"This animal, I think, is from another land," he said. "Never before have I seen a finer war-horse."

He turned to the silent figure to whom he had spoken and saw the Indian runner who had brought the unwelcome news to camp the evening before. He gazed with amazement at the sullen fierceness of the savage, who carried both tomahawk and knife. The Indian looked at him, and then looked away.

A young officer led to their horses two young females. The younger had golden hair and bright blue eyes. She smiled at the young man as he assisted her into the saddle. The other had shining black hair, skin rich in color, and a beautiful face.

The officer sprang into the saddle of the war-horse and bowed to Webb at the door of his cabin, and then they all moved away at a walk toward the north. The Indian runner suddenly moved by them and led the way along the military road.

Most words in italics indicate idioms. Their meanings are in the Glossary.

Chapter II

One of the women asked the officer who rode by her side, "Are such figures frequent in the woods, Heyward? If so, Cora and I shall need courage."

"The Indian is a runner for the army. He will guide us to the lake by a little-known path faster than the slow movements of the column."

"I like him not," said the lady. "You know him, Duncan, or you would not trust yourself to him?"

"Alice, I do know him. He is a Canadian, and yet he served with our friends the Mohawks. He stops; our path must be here."

When they reached the spot where the Indian stood, they saw a narrow path.

"Here then lies our way," said the young man in a low voice.

"Cora, what do you think?" asked the fair one.

"Should we distrust the man because his manners are not like ours and his skin is dark?" asked Cora.

Alice waited no longer, but followed the runner along the dark and tangled pathway. The young man opened the way for Cora. The servants followed the route of the column. Heyward said that their guide decided this to lessen the marks of their trail if the Canadian savages should be nearby. For many minutes the difficulty of the route allowed no further conversation. Then they came out of the bushes and entered the tall, dark forest. Here they moved at an easy pace. Suddenly, the sound of a horse's hoofs behind them caused the party to halt.

In a few moments, the strange man described in the earlier chapter came into view.

Heyward smiled as he watched the stranger. Alice made no effort to control her merriment, and even the thoughtful eye of Cora lighted with humor.

When the stranger had come close, he spoke. "I hear you are riding to William Henry, and I decided to join you for a more pleasant ride."

Heyward did not know if he should become angry or laugh at the other. "Are you a part of the army?"

The stranger answered, "No, I am a singing master."

"Heyward, allow him to journey in our party," cried Alice. "Besides," she added in a low voice, watching their sullen guide, "he may be a friend added to our strength in time of need."

"Do you think, Alice, that I would take those I love by this path if I feared danger?"

"No, no, I think not, but I like this strange man. Let us not refuse him. I am glad to meet you, friend, and I love to sing," continued the maiden.

"You have a soft and rich voice. I can carry one part, but we need two more singers. I always have the Psalms, hymns, and songs of the Old and New Testaments."

The stranger had drawn a book from his pocket and opened it. He took an instrument from his pocket, placed it in his mouth, and drew a high sound from it. Then he began singing.

The Indian spoke a few words in *broken English* to Heyward, who spoke to the stranger.

"We are not in danger, but common sense tells us to journey through this wilderness as quietly as possible. Alice, I must ask this gentleman to hold his song until a safer moment. Your safety, and that of Cora, is far more important to me than music." He turned his head quickly toward a bush and then looked suspiciously at their guide, who continued to move ahead. The young man smiled to himself, for he believed he had mistaken some shining leaf for the eyes of a hidden savage. Then he continued to ride forward.

Major Heyward should have been more watchful. After the group had passed, a fiercely wild face looked out at the travelers. His intended victims unknowingly rode onward through the forest.

Chapter III

A few miles westward, two men were resting on the ba. small stream, an hour's journey from Webb's camp. Whih had the red skin of a native of the woods, the other showea sunburnt skin of a white man. The Indian's body was neai naked and displayed an emblem of death, drawn in white ani black. He had no hair on his head except a scalping tuft, and his only ornament was an eagle's feather. A tomahawk and scalping knife were in his belt, while a short military rifle lay across his knee.

The white man was strong and thin. He wore a hunting shirt of forest green and a cap of skins. He also carried a knife in his belt but no tomahawk. He wore moccasins and a pair of leggings that laced at the sides. A pouch, a horn, and a rifle of great length were his equipment.

He spoke in the language known to all the natives of the country between the Hudson and the Potomac. "Your fathers came from the setting sun, crossed the big river, fought the people of the country, and took the land. Mine came from the red sky of the morning, over the *salt lake*, and did their work in the same way."

"Listen, Hawkeye," said the Indian, "the Mohicans came from the place where the sun hides at night, over great plains where the buffaloes live, until we reached the big river. There we fought our enemies till the ground was red with their blood. From the banks of the big river to the shores of the salt lake, there was none to meet us. The land we had taken like warriors, we kept like men. We drove our enemies into the woods with the bears.

"The first palefaces who came among us spoke no English. They came in a large canoe. Then, Hawkeye, we were one people, and we were happy. The salt lake gave us its fish, the wood its deer, and the air its birds. We took wives who gave us children, and we worshiped the Great Spirit.

"The Dutch landed and gave my people the firewater; they drank until the sky and the earth seemed to meet. Then they foolishly *parted with* their land. Foot by foot, the white man drove them back from the shores, and I, that am a chief, have never visited the land of my fathers. So all of my family departed, each at his time, to the land of spirits. I must go too, and when Uncas follows in my footsteps, there will no longer be any of our blood, for my boy is the last of the Mohicans."

"Uncas is here!" said another voice. "Who speaks to Uncas?"

The next moment a young warrior passed between the two men and seated himself on the bank of the stream. Chingachgook turned his eyes toward his son and demanded, "Do our enemies dare to leave the print of their moccasins in these woods?"

"I have been on their trail," replied the young Indian. "They number as many as the fingers of my two hands, but they lie hid like cowards."

"The thieves are waiting for scalps!" said the white man. "That busy Frenchman, Montcalm, has sent his spies!"

"Hawkeye, let us eat tonight and show them that we are men tomorrow."

"I am ready."

"Hugh!" exclaimed the older Indian, turning quickly.

"What do you hear, Chingachgook?"

"I hear the sound of feet! The horses of white men are coming! Hawkeye, they are your brothers; speak to them."

"I will. But I see nothing. Ha! Now I hear the bushes move, and here they come. God keep them from the Hurons!"

Chapter IV

The scout was still speaking when the leader of the party came into view.

"Who comes?" demanded the scout, throwing his rifle carelessly across his left arm and keeping one finger of his right hand on the trigger.

"Friends," returned Heyward. "Men who have journeyed since the rising sun and are sadly tired. Know you the distance to Fort William Henry? We left Fort Edward this morning for the head of the lake."

"Then you must have lost your eyesight before losing your way, for the road is wide."

"We trusted an Indian guide to take us by a shorter path, and he lied about his knowledge."

"An Indian lost in the woods!" said the scout. " 'Tis strange! How can an Indian be lost between Horican and the river? Is he a Mohawk?"

"Not by birth, but adopted in that tribe. He is a Huron."

The two companions of the scout sprang to their feet with surprise.

"A Huron!" repeated the scout. "They are thieves. Since you trusted one of them, I wonder that you have not met with more."

"I told you our guide is now a Mohawk, and he serves with our forces as a friend."

"And I tell you that he who is born a Huron will die a Huron," returned the scout.

"You have not yet answered my question," said Heyward, impatiently. "What is our distance from Fort Edward? If you will lead me there, I shall reward you."

"The Indian has deceived you and deserted?"

"Neither, I hope. He is in the rear."

"I should like to look at him," said the scout, entering the path. After a few steps, he met the females. Behind these, the runner leaned against a tree. He did not move as the scout examined him, but his look was dark and savage. The hunter gazed for a moment at the females and returned to Heyward.

"If we were alone, I could show you the way to Edward myself within an hour, but with ladies, 'tis impossible!"

"And why? They are tired, but they are quite able to ride a few more miles."

"I wouldn't walk a mile in these woods after dark with that runner."

"I confess I have been suspicious. I have tried to hide it from my companions. I would follow him no longer, but made him follow me. I believe the rascal has deceived me."

The hunter motioned his two red companions to his side. They spoke together quietly. His companions separated, taking opposite sides of the path.

"Now you go back," said the hunter to Heyward, "and hold the rascal in talk; these Mohicans will take him."

Heyward understood the dangers. The sun had already disappeared, and the woods were becoming dark. He left the scout, who immediately entered into a loud conversation with the stranger that had joined the travelers that morning. He rode to the sullen runner, who still leaned against the tree.

"You see, Magua," he said, "that the night is coming and yet we are not near William Henry. But happily, we have met a hunter who promises to lead us to a place where we may rest safely till the morning."

"Then The Sly Fox will go. Munro waits for me."

"Go! And what story will The Sly Fox tell Munro? Will you tell him that you left his children without a guide? Munro has promised you a gift for your services. Rest your legs and eat."

The Indian seated himself on the ground and began to eat, first looking carefully around him.

"You will find the path in the morning," continued Heyward. He paused, for sounds like the crack of a dried stick and the rustling of leaves came from the nearby bushes.

The hand of Magua dropped from his mouth to his side. He glanced about and raised himself to his feet. Heyward felt he must act. He dismounted and said, "Magua does not eat. Perhaps I may find something among my food that will please him."

When Magua felt the fingers of Heyward touch his own arm, he struck the young man and dived into the bushes. The next instant, Chingachgook appeared and moved across the path in swift pursuit. Next followed the shout of Uncas and the sharp report of the hunter's rifle.

Chapter V

The three foresters returned from their unsuccessful pursuit.

"Why stop so soon!" Heyward exclaimed. "The scoundrel must be hidden behind some of these trees. We are not safe while he is free."

"I heard him rushing over the dry leaves, *caught a glimpse* of him, and pulled the trigger, but I only skinned him."

"We are four strong men to one wounded man!"

"That red devil would draw you to the tomahawks of his companions before you began the chase. I should not have fired within sound of an ambush! Come, friends, let us move, or our scalps will be drying in front of Montcalm's tent tomorrow!"

"What can we do?" Heyward said, feeling totally helpless. "Desert me not, *for* God's *sake*!"

His companions spoke in the language of their tribe. Then the white man turned and said in English, "If you would save these females, you have no time to waste! These Mohicans and I will try to save them from harm. First, you must promise two things. The one is to be still as these sleeping woods, and the other is to keep the hiding place you shall see forever a secret."

"I will do my best."

"Then follow, for we are wasting time!"

When they rejoined the anxious females, Heyward told them of the need for their silence. Then they immediately moved to the water's edge to join the rest of the party.

"What to do with these horses!" muttered the white man. "We would lose time to cut their throats and throw them into the river. If we leave them here we tell our enemies that we are nearby! Let us try to make them think we are moving at a horse's speed."

The Indians led the frightened horses into the river. The horses would spend the night standing in the water, tied to some bushes. "Water leaves no trail, and that place is dark," said the scout.

The scout drew a canoe of bark from some bushes and motioned for the females to enter. As soon as Cora and Alice were seated, the scout held one side of the canoe and Heyward the other, and they carried it up against the stream, with the tall stranger following. Occasionally the scout would stop to listen for any sounds that might come from the forest. Then he would continue his slow progress.

At last, the scout told Heyward and his fellow travelers to seat themselves in the forward end of the canoe. He took the other end himself and, with a powerful push, sent his fragile canoe into the center of the violent stream.

The river here moved between high rocks. In front, the water seemed piled against the sky, and it tumbled into caverns. For many minutes, the passengers thought the fury of the stream was sweeping them to destruction. Just as Alice covered her eyes in horror, certain that they would be swept within the whirlpool at the foot of the falls, the canoe floated to the side of a flat rock.

"You are at the foot of Glenn's Falls," said the scout, speaking within the roar of the falls. "There, go on the rock, and I will bring up the Mohicans."

As the last foot touched the rock, the canoe sped away, and the scout disappeared in the darkness. The travelers remained, helpless, afraid to move along the rocks. In a few minutes, the canoe shot back and floated again at the side of the low rock.

"Have you or your two companions heard or seen anything of our enemies?" cried Heyward.

"The horses seem to smell wolves, and a wolf will stay near an Indian ambush."

The scout and the Mohicans moved by the group of travelers. The three disappeared, seeming to vanish against the dark rock.

Chapter VI

A sudden light flashed upon Heyward and his companions and showed the scout sitting at the further end of a narrow cave, holding a blazing log. At a little distance stood Uncas. The travelers gazed at the graceful, young Mohican. Each member of the party noticed the proud features of the young warrior. Heyward openly expressed his admiration.

"Let us hope," he said, "that this Mohican may be a brave and true friend."

"He who looks at him remembers the color of his skin!" said Cora.

The scout called to them to enter.

"Are we quite safe in this cave?" demanded Heyward. "Is there no danger of surprise?"

Chingachgook took a blazing log, lifted a blanket, and showed that the cave had two openings. Then he crossed a deep, narrow split in the rocks which was open to the sky and entered another cave like theirs.

"Old foxes like Chingachgook and myself are not often caught in a den with one hole," said Hawkeye, laughing. "The fall was once below us. But the water has fallen back some hundred feet and left the center of the river dry, first working out these two little holes for us to hide in."

"We are then on an island?"

"Aye! There are the falls on two sides of us, and the river above and below."

They now turned their attention to their supper. The meal was refreshing to the tired party. Uncas served the females. Heyward knew that Indians did not usually perform any work for women. Hospitality, however, was sacred among them. While the young chief offered Alice the sweet water and the dried meat with courtesy, in serving her sister, his dark eye gazed on her face, and once or twice he spoke in English.

"Come, friend," said Hawkeye to the tall stranger, "how do you name yourself?"

"David Gamut," returned the singing master.

"A very good name, sir. What is your work?"

11

"I teach singing to the young men of Connecticut."

"You might be better employed. They go laughing and singing too much through the woods when they ought to breathe quietly. Can you handle a rifle?"

"I have never touched deadly weapons!"

"You carry news for the general sometimes?"

"Never; my only work is instruction in sacred music!"

" 'Tis strange work," muttered Hawkeye. "Well, friend, I suppose it is your talent. Let us hear what you can do. 'Twill be a friendly manner of saying good night."

"With pleasure I agree," said David, opening his little book. Alice and Cora joined David, and the song began.

The Indians listened with an attention that seemed to turn them into stone. But the scout remembered his boyhood when he had heard these songs. Suddenly, a cry that seemed not human rose in the air.

"What is it?" murmured Alice.

"What is it?" repeated Heyward.

Neither Hawkeye nor the Indians replied. Their manner showed their astonishment. Then they spoke together, and Uncas cautiously left the cave. When he had gone, the scout spoke.

"No one here knows it. I thought I had heard every cry that Indian or beast could make, but I was wrong! Well, Uncas," he said to the young chief as he returned, "what see you?"

The answer was short.

"There is nothing outside," continued Hawkeye, "and our hiding place is in darkness. Pass into the other cave and seek sleep. We must be up and moving long before the sun."

Cora and Alice obeyed, and Duncan followed.

"Leave us not, Duncan," said Alice. "We cannot sleep with that horrid cry *ringing in our ears*!"

"Sleep is necessary to you both," he answered.

"I may agree with you, but I cannot do it," returned Cora. "Heyward, we daughters cannot forget the anxiety of our father, knowing his children are lost in this wilderness!"

"He is a soldier."

"He is a father, also."

Suddenly the same horrid cry as before filled the air. The scout raised the blanket and stood in the opening with a look on his face that showed he faced a mystery beyond his experience.

Chapter VII

The party came out from the cave. Each person looked anxiously for some signs of life that might explain the noise they had heard, but they saw only rocks and trees.

Once more the same sound rose from the river.

"I know that sound," said Duncan, "for often have I heard it on the field of battle. A horse will give that shriek in pain or in terror. In the open air I know it well."

"The wolves must be near them, and the frightened beasts are calling for help," said the scout.

The natives placed themselves in positions which gave a view of both shores. Heyward placed some leaves on the rocks for the two sisters. He sat nearby, and David sat among the rocks.

Hours passed without further interruption. Duncan made a pillow of the rock. David began to snore. Hawkeye and the Mohicans lay, watching the shore of the stream. Finally, a soft light above the treetops announced the approach of day. Then Hawkeye shook Duncan from sleep.

"Now is the time to journey," he whispered. "Be silent but quick."

Duncan moved to the sleeping females.

"Cora! Alice! Awake! The hour has come to move!"

At that instant, a roar of yells and cries filled the woods, the caves, the rocks, the river, and the air. David raised himself, exclaiming, "What man can make sounds like these!"

The reports of a number of rifles from the opposite bank of the stream followed his words and left the singing master senseless on the rock. Just then a stream of flame came from the rock, and a shriek announced that Hawkeye had found a victim. At this, the attackers retreated and the place became still once more. Duncan used the moment to carry the body of Gamut to shelter.

"After he has slept a while, he will be a wiser man," said Hawkeye. "The Hurons will come again with new plans to master our scalps."

A long and anxious watch followed, and Duncan began to hope that their enemies had left, but Hawkeye said, "There were forty of them yelling this morning! And they know our number too well to give up. Look into the water above, just where it flows over the rocks. The devils have swum down and hit the head of the island."

Heyward lifted his head and saw a miracle of skill. The river had worn away the rock, and the first part of the fall was less abrupt than is usual at waterfalls. A party of the Indians had entered the water and swum down to the point. He could see four heads above a few logs that were caught on the rocks. The next moment, he saw a fifth Huron floating over the edge of the fall. The savage struggled powerfully to reach the point. He was stretching out an arm, when he shot away and fell suddenly over the deep falls. One wild shriek rose from below, and all was still again.

"Prepare for a close struggle while I fire on their rush," demanded Hawkeye.

At that moment, four savages sprang from behind the logs. When they were within a few feet, the rifle of Hawkeye slowly rose among the bushes and poured out its deadly shot. The first Indian fell among the rocks.

"Now, Uncas!" cried the scout, drawing his long knife. "Take the last of the scoundrels; of the other two we are certain!"

Uncas obeyed, and only two enemies remained. Heyward and Hawkeye rushed down a little slope toward their enemies.

"Come on, ye bloody-minded dogs!" muttered the scout. He met a huge savage. At the same moment, Duncan fought with the other *hand-to-hand*. Hawkeye and his opponent struggled, but the Indian slowly *gave way* before the force of the scout, who suddenly drove the knife to his heart. In the meantime, Heyward was in a deadly struggle at the edge of the falls. Heyward felt the hands of the other at his throat. At that instant, a swift knife appeared before him. Blood flowed from the Indian's arm, and while the arm of Uncas drew Duncan backward, his enemy fell over the precipice.

The young Mohican gave a shout of triumph, and with Duncan following, he moved up the slope and sought the friendly shelter of the rocks.

Chapter VIII

The moment the struggle was over, a wild yell rose in the air, followed by the flashes of rifles.

"Let them burn their powder," said the scout.

"That bullet was better aimed than most!" cried Duncan as shot struck the rock at his side.

Uncas pointed to a tree growing on the opposite bank of the river. At the top, hiding behind the trunk, they saw a savage. Uncas and the scout fired together. The leaves and bark of the tree flew into the air, but the Indian answered with a laugh and another bullet.

At last, the Huron attempted a better aim. The quick eyes of the Mohicans saw his exposed legs. Their rifles made one report, and sinking on his wounded legs, part of his body came into view. Hawkeye shot, the rifle fell, and the savage swung in the wind while he still grasped a branch of the tree. Then the savage grasped wildly at empty air for an instant, and the body parted the bubbling waters.

"Uncas, go down to the canoe and bring up the big horn. It is all the powder we have left, and we shall need it. My horn is empty, as is my pouch."

The young Mohican obeyed, but soon called with a loud exclamation. The companions rushed together down to the deep split. The whole party saw their little boat floating toward the swift current of the river, directed by an adventurous Huron. He raised his head above the canoe, waved his hand, and gave a shout of success. A yell and a laugh from the woods answered his cry.

"What can we do?" demanded Duncan. "What will *become of* us?"

Hawkeye passed his finger around the tip of his head in a manner that made his meaning clear.

"Why die!" said Cora. "The path is open. Fly, then, to the woods! Go, brave men! You have done too much already; let us no longer keep you here!"

"The downstream current might soon carry us beyond the reach of their rifles," returned Hawkeye.

"Then try the river. Why stay to add to the number of the victims?"

"Because," repeated the scout, "a man should die at peace with himself rather than live with evil memories! What could we tell Munro when he asked about his children?"

"Go to him, and say that you left them with a message to hurry to their aid," returned Cora.

"There is sense in her words! Chingachgook! Uncas! Hear you the talk of the dark-eyed woman!"

He now spoke to his companions. The older Mohican heard him silently. After a moment of hesitation, he waved his hand in agreement and spoke the English word, "Good!" Then the warrior moved to the edge of the rock, dropped into the water, and sank from before their eyes.

The scout spoke to the generous girl.

"If they lead you into the woods, break the twigs on the bushes as you pass, and depend on having a friend who will follow to the ends of the earth before he deserts you."

He gave Cora a friendly shake of the hand and moved to the place where Chingachgook had just disappeared. For an instant, he looked about him and said sadly, "Had the powder *held out*, this could not have happened!" Then the water closed above his head, and he also became lost to view.

Uncas stood leaning against a rock. Cora pointed to the river and said, "Your friends are now probably safe. Is it not time for you to follow?"

"Uncas will stay," the young Mohican calmly answered in English.

"Go, young man. Go to my father and tell him to trust you with the money to buy the freedom of his daughters. Go! I wish you to go!"

The young chief no longer hesitated. He dropped into the stream, and they saw him no more.

Cora turned and addressed herself to Heyward.

"Follow the wise example set by these faithful men. To us, you can be of no further service here, but you may save your life."

He made no reply, but his eyes fell on the beautiful form of Alice, who was holding his arm like a child.

"There are evils worse than death," said Duncan, "and I may turn them away."

Cora ceased her talking and drew Alice after her into the deepest part of the inner cave.

Chapter IX

The stillness now around him seemed to Heyward like a dream. He listened at first for sounds that would tell him the fortune of those who had left. However, with the disappearance of Uncas, every sign of their guides was lost.

Duncan looked about him carefully but saw no sign of the approach of their hidden enemies. The wooded banks of the river seemed again deserted. Duncan began to hope for success.

"I cannot see the Hurons," he said to David, who had not recovered from the blow he had received. "Let us hide ourselves in the cave and trust in God."

"I have been asleep," said David, pressing his hand to his forehead. "Is the air still filled with shrieks and cries?"

"Not now," answered Heyward. "They have ceased." He led David into the cave, took some branches, and covered the opening. "Cora, I know your own courage will help you, but can we dry the tears of your sister?"

"I am calmer, Duncan," said Alice, forcing an appearance of calm through her tears, "much calmer now. Surely in this hidden spot, we are safe. We will hope everything from those generous men who have risked so much already."

"Now our gentle Alice speaks like a daughter of Munro!" said Heyward, pausing to press her hand. He then seated himself in the center of the cave, grasping his gun. "The Hurons, if they come, will not take us as easily as they think," he muttered, and he watched the opening to the cave.

A long silence followed his words. As minute after minute passed, a feeling of hope came to everyone. However, each one hesitated to speak, for fear the next moment would destroy that hope.

At last, David began to sing.

"May this not be dangerous?" asked Cora, glancing at Major Heyward.

"Others cannot hear his voice above the sound of the falls," was the answer. "Let him sing."

The voice of the singer filled the narrow cave, but softly because of his weakness. The song was sweet and calmed those who heard it. Alice dried her tears. Cora smiled on Gamut, and

Heyward turned his eyes from the cave's opening to look at David and at Alice. Suddenly, a yell burst into the air outside and instantly stilled David.

"We are lost!" exclaimed Alice, throwing herself into the arms of Cora.

"Not yet, not yet," returned the upset but brave Heyward. "The sound came from the center of the island; they have found their dead companions. They have not yet discovered us, so there is still hope."

A second yell followed the first. The sounds quickly spread around them in every direction. They heard cries near the two caves, from above and on every side of them.

Heyward heard voices near the hidden entrance to the cave, at the spot where the white man had abandoned his rifle. A burst of voices shouted together, "The Long Rifle!" Heyward well remembered this was the name the Indians had given to a famous hunter and scout for the English. He now learned for the first time that this had been his recent companion.

The savages searched for their enemy's body. More than once they brushed the branches, causing the leaves to rustle and the branches to crack.

The Indians left the cave and rushed outside again. Duncan looked at his companions.

"They are gone, Cora!" he whispered. "Alice, we are saved!"

"I will give my thanks to God," exclaimed the younger sister, and she seemed ready to pour out thanksgivings. But when her lips moved, the words they should have spoken appeared frozen by some new and sudden chill. She became pale as death, and her eyes filled with horror. Heyward turned, and looking above the ledge, he saw the evil, fierce, and savage features of Magua.

Duncan aimed his gun and fired. When the smoke had cleared, Magua was gone. Rushing to the opening, Heyward saw him stealing around a low ledge which soon hid him from sight.

Magua raised his voice in a long whoop. Before Duncan had time to recover from the shock, the Indians scattered his little cover of branches, entered the cave at both ends, and dragged him and his companions from their shelter to the outside. There the whole group of triumphant Hurons surrounded them.

Chapter X

The warriors approached their prisoners, speaking fiercely. Duncan looked about for Magua.

"Sly Fox, what do my conquerors say?"

"They ask for the hunter called The Long Rifle! The Hurons want the life of The Long Rifle, or they will have the blood of them that hide him!"

"He has escaped. He is beyond their reach."

Magua *shook his head* unbelievingly.

"Is he a bird, to spread his wings, or is he a fish, to swim without air? The Hurons are not fools!"

"He is no fish, yet The Long Rifle can swim. He floated down the stream."

"And why did the white chief stay?" demanded the Indian.

"The white man thinks only cowards desert their women," said the young man.

"Can the Mohicans swim, too? Where are The Great Snake and The Bounding Elk?"

Duncan replied, "They also went down the water."

When Heyward ceased to speak, Magua pointed to the river and muttered a few words to the Hurons. The savages raised a frightful yell of disappointment. Some ran furiously to the water's edge; others spat upon the ground. One or two even made frightening gestures toward their prisoners.

The leader now called his warriors to himself. Their meeting was short, and all seemed to agree on the decision.

The Indians had reached the island by carrying a canoe through the wood around the falls. They had set it in the water across from the upper part of the island and had placed their arms in it. Then several men holding to its sides had trusted themselves to two warriors who controlled the canoe. They now placed the light boat in the water, and the prisoners had to enter. Then the vessel floated down the current, and in a few moments the prisoners found themselves on the south bank of the stream. Here the Indians led from the bushes the horses, whose panic had caused their misfortune. The Indians now divided themselves. The larger group crossed the river, leaving the prisoners with six savages, headed by Magua.

Magua then signed to Heyward to assist the sisters into the saddles. David and Duncan journeyed on foot. Duncan hoped this might allow him to slow the speed of the party.

They continued in silence toward the south, in a direction nearly opposite to the road to William Henry. They passed through miles of the endless woods. Heyward knew that each step was carrying him further from the war and from his duty.

Cora alone remembered the parting instructions of the scout, and whenever an opportunity offered, she stretched out her arm to break a twig. But the watchful Indians made this act difficult and dangerous. Once, and once only, was she completely successful; that was when she broke down the branch of a large bush and let her glove fall at the same instant. One of the Indians observed her, and he returned the glove and laid his hand on his tomahawk with a look that put an end to her attempts.

Magua, during all this time, continued to move forward swiftly across brooks and over hills with the directness of a bird.

He suddenly climbed a steep and difficult hill, and the sisters had to dismount to follow. When they reached the top, they found themselves on a level spot thinly covered with trees. Under one of these, Magua had thrown his dark form, ready now to seek the rest which the whole party needed.

Chapter XI

Heyward said to Magua, who sat apart from the others, "The chief of William Henry will reward Magua for the return of his daughters."

"Is the heart of the white-headed chief soft when he thinks of his babes? He is hard to his warriors, and his eyes are made of stone!"

"You have seen the grayhead in front of his warriors, Magua, but I have seen his eyes swimming in water when he spoke of those children!"

An expression crossed the dark features of the Indian and became so fierce that Duncan felt some evil desire caused it.

"Go," said the Huron, calmly. "Go to the dark-haired daughter, and say Magua waits to speak."

Duncan slowly moved to the sisters.

"Remember," Duncan reminded Cora, "your life and Alice's may depend on your calmness and cleverness."

Cora moved to the native and said, "What would The Sly Fox say to the daughter of Munro?"

"Magua was born a chief among the Hurons of the lakes. His Canada fathers taught him to drink the firewater, and he became a rascal. The Hurons chased him away. Who gave Magua the firewater? Who made him a villain? 'Twas the palefaces. The old chief, your father, made a law that he would punish any Indian who swallowed the firewater and came into the wigwams of the white warriors. Magua foolishly opened his mouth, and the hot firewater led him into the cabin of Munro. What did the grayhead do?"

"He punished you," said the daughter.

"Magua was not himself; the firewater spoke and acted for him! But Munro tied the Huron chief before all the pale-faced warriors and beat him like a dog. The scars of knives and bullets — a warrior may brag of these before his nation — but the grayhead has left marks on the back of the Huron chief that he must hide under a cloth."

"What would you have, Magua?" said Cora, struggling to speak with calmness. "*At least* free my sister, and pour out all your hate on me."

"The light eyes can go back to the Horican if the dark-haired woman will go back with Magua to his tribe and live in his wigwam forever."

Cora replied, "What joy would Magua find in sharing his cabin with a wife he did not love?"

The Indian answered with deep hate:

"The daughter of Munro would draw Magua's water, tend his corn, and cook his meat. The Sly Fox would have a woman slave to beat and would hurt the heart of the grayhead."

"Monster!" cried Cora. "Only a devil could think of such revenge!"

The Indian smiled and motioned her away. He approached his companions and spoke of the battle at the caves; he named the name of The Long Rifle. He pointed toward the captives and spoke of the wives and children of the dead. Then he demanded:

"Must the Hurons bear this? Who shall say to wives and mothers that we have not taken revenge! What shall we say to the old men when they ask us for scalps? We must take blood!"

The whole group sprang to their feet and drew their knives. Two warriors tied Heyward to a tree, and another tied the singing master. On Duncan's right was Cora; on his left the trembling Alice.

The Hurons prepared to kill their prisoners. Some made a pile; others prepared spears of wood.

Magua approached Cora. "Ha! What says the daughter of Munro? Is her head too good to find a pillow in the wigwam of The Sly Fox?"

"What means the monster?" demanded Heyward.

"Shall I send the yellow hair to her father, and will you follow Magua to the great lakes?"

"Did he speak of sending me to our father?" asked the trembling Alice.

For many moments the elder sister looked upon the younger. At last she spoke with gentleness.

"Alice," she said, "the Huron offers to return Duncan and you to our father if I will follow him to the wilderness and remain there to become his wife! Speak then, Alice! And you, too, Major Heyward. Guide me between you for I am wholly yours."

"Cora! Cora!" cried the astonished young man. "The thought is worse than a thousand deaths."

"I knew that would be *your* answer!" exclaimed Cora. "What says my Alice?"

Alice said, "No, no, we must die as we have lived: together!"

"Then die!" shouted Magua with rage, throwing his tomahawk at the speaker. The ax shivered in the tree above Alice's head. The sight maddened Duncan. He broke the ropes which held him and rushed upon another savage. They fell to the earth together. His opponent rose and pressed Duncan to the ground. Duncan saw the knife shining in the air when a whistling sound swept past him, and he heard the sharp crack of a rifle. His enemy's eyes stared, and the Indian fell dead by his side.

Chapter XII

The Hurons stood in shock. The next moment Hawkeye advanced upon them from the bushes, waving his rifle like a club. A form leaped into the center of the Hurons, swinging a tomahawk and waving a knife in front of Cora. Another shape moved to his side. The Hurons uttered the well-known names:

"The Long Rifle! The Bounding Elk! The Great Snake!"

Magua rushed with his knife upon Chingachgook, and a hand-to-hand battle began.

Uncas leaped on an enemy, and with a blow of his tomahawk, split him to the brain. Hawkeye got another enemy with one sweep of his weapon and crushed him to the earth. Heyward tore the weapon of Magua from the tree, sprang upon one Indian, and found he needed all his courage to defend himself. The next moment Hawkeye's rifle fell on the head of his opponent, and he sank from the arms of Duncan.

The fifth Huron sprang toward Cora, sending his sharp ax before him. The tomahawk skinned her shoulder and cut the ropes which tied her to the tree. She flew to Alice and tried to tear the ropes from her sister. The Huron seized Cora by her hair. But Uncas sprang through the air and landed on the chest of his enemy, driving him many yards from the spot. They rose together and fought until the knife of Uncas reached the Huron's heart.

The Sly Fox and The Great Snake were still struggling, covered with dust and blood, at the edge of the little plain. The Mohican made a powerful thrust with his knife. Magua suddenly fell backward, seemingly without life. His opponent leaped to his feet, shouting in triumph.

"Victory to the Mohican!" cried Hawkeye, raising his rifle to offer the finishing blow.

But at that very moment, the Huron rolled swiftly over the edge of the precipice, and falling on his feet, went leaping into the bushes. The Mohicans followed with speed, but the scout called them back.

"Let him go, let him go. 'Tis but one man, and he is without rifle or bow, many a long mile from his comrades. He can do no more mischief now."

Uncas and Heyward flew to the assistance of the females, and quickly freeing Alice, placed her in the arms of Cora.

Hawkeye freed David from the ropes.

"Friend," said David, "I thank you that the hairs of my head still grow where God placed them."

"It is nothing," returned the scout. "I have got back my old rifle, and that is a victory. These Hurons made a mistake when they placed their weapons out of reach. Had Uncas or his father had patience, we should have come in with three bullets and finished the whole pack."

David seated himself and said, "I invite you, friends, to join me in giving thanks for our rescue." He raised his voice and sang a sacred song.

The scout announced that they must move. They went down the steep sides of the hill and found the horses at the foot, near a clear and sparkling spring of bright water.

While the guides were preparing a meal, Heyward spoke to the scout.

"How do we see you so soon, without aid from Fort Edward?"

"Had we gone there, we would have been too late to save your scalps. We lay by the bank of the Hudson, watching the movements of the Hurons. The trail led us on to the broken bush."

When they had completed their meal, each took a long parting drink at the spring. The whole party mounted and moved swiftly along the narrow path toward the north, leaving the spring and the bodies of the dead.

Chapter XIII

The route Hawkeye took lay across the sandy plains which the party had traveled on the morning of the same day. The sun had now fallen low, but long before dark they had made many miles on their return. Hawkeye pointed toward the setting sun.

"That is the signal for us to rest," he said. "Our night, however, will soon be over. With the moon, we must be up and moving again. Nearby is a small fort to protect us."

The hunter moved into a thicket. After a few hundred feet, he entered an open space that surrounded a low, green mound. On this mound was an old building quietly falling to pieces in the forest. The roof had fallen, but the walls still stood.

The sisters gladly dismounted and prepared to enjoy their halt in the coolness of the evening.

"Few know the house is here," said Hawkeye. "I was young and went out with the Mohicans to fight the Mohawks. Forty days and forty nights we fought, and not a man of them lived to tell the story. I did not like the thought that humans like myself should lay on the ground for beasts to tear. I buried the dead with my own hands, under that very mound."

Heyward and the sisters rose immediately from the grass in horror.

"They are gone," continued Hawkeye. "They'll never shout the war whoop nor strike a blow with the tomahawk again! And of all those who fought them, Chingachgook and I only are living!"

The hunter and his companions prepared for the comfort and protection of those they guided. They roofed in a corner of the building to keep out the dew, and laid piles of sweet shrubs and dried leaves beneath it for the sisters to rest on.

The sisters soon sank into slumber. Duncan prepared to watch near them, but the scout pointed toward Chingachgook and said, "The Mohican will be our guard; therefore, let us sleep. Do like Uncas and myself. Sleep, and sleep in safety."

Heyward saw that the younger Indian had thrown his form on the side of the mound while they were talking, and David had followed his example. The young man and Hawkeye soon fell asleep, and a deep silence covered the spot.

A light touch on the shoulder awakened Duncan.

"The Mohicans hear an enemy!" whispered Hawkeye. "Lead the horses into the fort, Uncas."

The sounds of approaching footsteps were now plain. They soon mixed with voices calling to each other in the Huron language.

Duncan grasped his rifle firmly. Soon the Hurons were beating the bushes and gradually approaching the edge of the thicket which encircled the little area.

Duncan saw the trembling sisters in the far corner of the building, and the Mohicans standing in the shadow, ready to strike when necessary. At that instant the thicket opened, and a tall and armed Huron advanced into the open space. As he gazed upon the silent fort, he made an exclamation of surprise and called in a low voice to a companion.

They stood together for several moments. They then approached with slow and cautious steps. The foot of one of them suddenly rested on the mound, and he stooped to examine it.

The savages were so near that the least motion in one of the horses, or even a loud breath, would have exposed the fugitives. The Hurons spoke together, their voices low and solemn. Then they drew back, keeping their eyes on the ruin, and disappeared.

Hawkeye drew a long breath and exclaimed in a whisper:

"Aye! They respect the dead, and it has this time saved their own lives, and perhaps ours too."

Heyward heard the two Hurons gather their companions, who listened to their report. After a few minutes of solemn conversation, the sounds grew more distant and finally were lost in the forest.

Hawkeye waited until a signal from Chingachgook told him that their enemies were gone. Then he motioned to Heyward to bring out the horses and to assist the sisters into their saddles. The instant this was done, they left the silent and crumbling ruin and disappeared into the woods.

Chapter XIV

Until the party was deep in the forest, no one spoke. The scout halted more than once to speak with the Mohicans, pointing upward at the moon and examining the bark of trees with care. The guides led on toward a distant river.

When they reached the banks of the little stream, they entered the water. For an hour they traveled in the bed of the brook, leaving no trail. They left the stream and crossed a wooded plain. The path soon became more uneven, and the travelers saw mountains.

Hawkeye led his followers deep within the shadows of these mountains. The route now lay over ground ragged with rocks, and their progress was slow. At last the party began to climb a steep hill. The thick darkness began to disappear, and when they came from the woods onto a flat and mossy rock at the top of the mountain, they met the morning.

The travelers saw the southern shore of the Horican below them. To the north stretched the "holy lake," with its many islands. To the south stretched the plain.

On the western shore of the lake lay the buildings of William Henry and the white tents of a camp of ten thousand Frenchmen. Even while the travelers looked down, the roar of cannons rose from the valley.

"We are too late!" said the scout. "Montcalm has already filled the woods with his Indians. But if you will follow, I will make a push. We shall use the approaching fog as a cover."

He threw himself down the steep slope, and in a few minutes they were all far down the mountain.

"We shall be as likely to walk into the French guards as to pass them in the fog!" said the scout.

"Can we make a circle to avoid the danger?" asked Heyward.

"If we turn from the line of march in a fog, we won't find it again! Come, the fog is shutting in."

Heyward placed himself between the sisters and drew them swiftly forward, keeping the dim figure of their leader in sight. They had gone over half the distance to the friendly fort when they heard:

"Qui va la'?"

"Push on!" whispered the scout.

A dozen voices renewed the cry.

"Ami de la France," cried Duncan, dragging the sisters onward.

"You are an enemy of France! Fire, men, fire!"

Fifty rifles exploded. Happily, the aim was bad. They heard the order to fire again.

"We shall bring their whole army upon us," said Duncan. "Lead on, friend, for your life and ours."

The cries of voices calling to each other and the reports of rifles were now on every side of them. Suddenly, a strong light flashed, the fog rolled upward, and several cannon roared across the plain.

" 'Tis from the fort!" exclaimed Hawkeye.

Uncas took the arm of Cora. Men in pursuit were on their footsteps, and each instant threatened their capture or their destruction.

"Stand firm, and be ready, my brave 60ths!" exclaimed a voice above them.

"Father! Father! It is Alice! Save us!"

"Hold!" shouted the first speaker. " 'Tis she! To the field! Pull no trigger, or you kill my lambs! Drive off these dogs of France with your steel."

Duncan heard the opening of a large gate and met a long line of warriors. An officer of huge frame rushed out of the fog and hugged Cora and Alice to his chest, while he exclaimed:

"For this I thank thee, God! Let danger come as it will, thy servant is now prepared!"

Chapter XV

The siege continued. Munro had no means of defense. Webb, whose army lay on the banks of the Hudson, seemed to have forgotten his countrymen.

On the fifth day of the siege, Major Heyward was on the wall of the fort when he saw the scout advancing toward the fort under the guard of a French officer. The face of Hawkeye was pale and his manner discouraged. He was without his favorite weapon, and his arms were tied behind him.

Heyward moved rapidly across the parade ground to Munro's apartment.

"I am sorry to see, sir," he said, "that the messenger I suggested has returned, a captive of the French!"

"Montcalm got him and sent him in," said the old colonel. "There is a letter, too. He keeps the letter while he frees the messenger. And yet we must know more about that letter!"

"Our decision should be speedy," said Duncan. "We cannot hold the fort much longer. More than half our guns are broken. The walls are falling *about our ears*, and supplies become low. Even the men show signs of alarm."

"Major Heyward," said Munro, "I have served my king for half a century; I know all you say. But, while there is hope, this fortress will I defend. We need to see the letter. Then we will know Webb's plans. The Marquis of Montcalm has invited me to an interview. I wish you to go for me."

Duncan cheerfully agreed to take Munro's place in the interview. The young man received instruction, and then, under the protection of a white flag of truce, left the fort. A French officer met him and took him to the tent of the leader of the French army.

The enemy general received the young messenger, in the presence of his officers and a group of the native chiefs. Heyward paused when he saw the evil face of Magua. He controlled his emotions and turned to the enemy leader, who had already advanced to meet him.

"Sir," said the general in French, "it gives me much pleasure. Ah, do you need an interpreter?"

"It is not necessary," Heyward replied. "I speak a little French."

"Ah, good," said Montcalm, taking Duncan into the tent, out of earshot. "Your commandant is a brave man. But, sir, it is time to think more of human life and less of courage. I hope, sir, you come with authority to discuss surrender? I should be sorry to have the defense continue; that will anger my red friends. I find it difficult, even now, to control them. Shall we speak of surrender?"

"You are incorrect, sir, about the strength of William Henry. There is also a powerful force within a few hours' march of us."

"And their leader wisely judges them to be safer in their fort than in the field."

Montcalm then tried to persuade his guest to discuss surrender. *On the other hand*, Heyward tried to find out about the letter. Neither succeeded, however, and after a long interview, Duncan left and returned to the fort and to the quarters of his own commander.

Chapter XVI

Major Heyward found Munro with his daughters. When they saw Duncan, Cora led Alice from the room. Munro paced the room for a few moments. At last he raised his eyes and exclaimed:

"They are a pair of excellent girls, Heyward. You wished to speak of this the day you arrived. I am now ready to hear you."

"I have a message from Montcalm —"

"Let the Frenchman *go to the devil*, sir!" exclaimed the colonel. "I wish to discuss my family. Your mother was the only child of my best friend, Duncan, and I'll now hear you."

Duncan replied, "My request, as you know, sir, was to ask the honor of being your son."

"Have you spoken to Cora?"

"Cora! I did not mention her name," said Duncan, stammering.

"And whom did you wish to marry, Major Heyward?"

"You have another lovely child."

"Alice!" exclaimed the father in astonishment.

"Such was my wish, sir."

Munro paced the room rapidly. At last, he paused in front of Heyward and said, "Duncan Heyward, I have loved you. But you wish to be my son, and you are ignorant of my history. I was your age when I promised to marry Alice Graham. But the marriage was not acceptable to her father. I left the country in the service of my king and fought in many different lands before duty called me to the West Indies. There I married a woman who became the mother of Cora. My wife was the daughter of a gentleman of those isles. Her mother was descended from a slave. Ha! Major Heyward, in your part of the country people believe these unfortunate people inferior."

" 'Tis unfortunately true, sir," said Duncan.

"And you hate to mix the blood of the Heywards with one so lowly — even if she is lovely and noble?" fiercely demanded the jealous parent.

"God keep me from such prejudice!" returned Duncan. "The sweetness, the beauty, of your younger daughter, Colonel Munro, might explain my love."

"You are right, sir," returned the old man, gently. "When death took my wife, I returned to Scotland. Would you believe it, Duncan! The angel had remained faithful for twenty years, and she took me for her husband."

"And became the mother of Alice?" exclaimed Duncan.

"She did," said the old man, "and died giving me that blessing. I had her but one year, a short time of happiness."

Suddenly the old man rose, approached his companion, and demanded:

"Have you, Major Heyward, some communication that I should hear from Montcalm?"

Duncan immediately gave him the message.

"I will meet the Frenchman *at once*, sir. Go, and send out a messenger to let them know I am coming."

The young man went to make the necessary arrangements. Soon they left the fort with an escort.

Montcalm moved toward them, spoke words of greeting, and opened their discussion.

"I have asked for this interview because I hope I can persuade you of the impossibility of fighting my troops. These hills allow us to see into your fort, and I know your weakness."

"Can you see to the Hudson and the army of Webb? I expect him soon."

"Let General Webb be his own interpreter," returned Montcalm, holding a letter toward Munro.

The old soldier seized the paper eagerly. As his eye passed over the words, his expression changed from a look of pride to one of shame. Letting the paper fall from his hand, Colonel Munro bowed his head in deep sadness. Duncan caught the letter and read its message. General Webb advised a speedy surrender and said he could not come to their rescue.

"We are still masters of the fort," cried Duncan. "Let us fight for our lives."

"My boy," exclaimed the old man, "we will go back and dig our graves behind those walls."

"Sirs," said Montcalm, "listen to my plan before you leave me. We must destroy the fort, but you and your brave comrades need not die. Keep your colors and your arms. You may surrender in an honorable way."

The commander heard him with amazement.

"I have lived to see two things in my old age that never did I expect to see," Munro said. "An Englishman afraid to support a friend, and an honest Frenchman." After that, he again dropped his head to his chest and returned slowly toward the fort.

Duncan remained to decide the plan of surrender. Munro would surrender the fort in the morning. The soldiers would keep their arms, their colors, their supplies, and therefore, their honor.

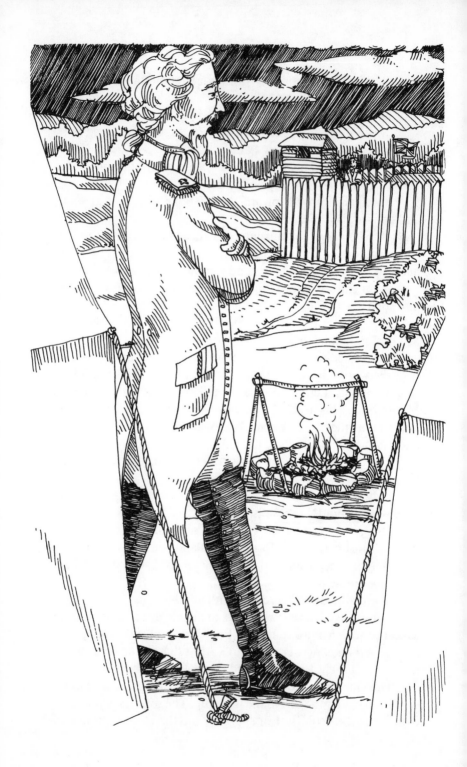

Chapter XVII

During the night of the ninth of August, 1757, Montcalm walked from a large tent in the French camp and gazed at the walls of the nearby fort. He saw a figure on the wall, looking at the tents of the French camp. He saw the large frame of the man and knew that it was Munro.

The Frenchman saw a rifle slowly rise within a few feet of him, but before the owner could fire it, Montcalm's hand was on the lock. Montcalm demanded:

"What means this! Magua knows that the English and the French have *buried the hatchet*."

"Not a Huron warrior has a scalp," returned Magua, "and the palefaces make friends! Magua took the hatchet to color it with blood. When it is red, we shall bury it. Teach your young men it is peace. The Sly Fox knows how to speak to a Huron warrior."

Without further words, the savage moved silently toward the woods and his own tribe.

Montcalm returned to his tent, giving the order to wake the army.

Within the fort, soldiers shouldered their empty guns. Women and children ran from place to place. Munro appeared among his troops, firm but discouraged. Duncan found the sisters, in the middle of a group of weeping females.

"I must seek a protector for you," said Heyward.

The sounds of music *caught his ear*, and he found David. In a few words, Duncan explained his wishes.

"I will care for them," replied Gamut.

"None should approach the ladies with rudeness. If any Indians disturb them, threaten to report them to Montcalm. A word will be enough."

The English column was now moving, and Alice and Cora left the parade ground with the crowd that surrounded them.

As the timid group of women left the protection of the fort, they saw the whole scene. On the right, the French army stood at attention. The English, numbering nearly three thousand, were moving slowly across the plain. Along the edge of the woods hung a dark cloud of savages watching their enemies.

As the female crowd approached the Indians, Magua placed his hands to his mouth and gave a yell. More than two thousand savages broke from the forest at the signal and threw themselves across the plain. Death was everywhere. The flow of blood was like a river.

The English soldiers tried to stop their attackers, but the Indians tore their unloaded rifles from their hands.

The sisters stood horrified and helpless. On every side rose shrieks, cries, and yells. Then Alice dropped senseless to the earth, and Cora sank to her side.

"Lady," said Gamut, "this is not a place for Christians. Let us fly."

"Go," said Cora, looking at her unconscious sister. "Save yourself."

David looked for a moment at the dark forms on every side of him and seemed to grow taller.

"The boy David tamed the evil spirit of Saul with song. I will try the power of music here."

Then, raising his voice, he poured out a powerful song. The sounds caught the ear of Magua, who uttered a yell of pleasure when he saw them at his mercy.

"Come," he said, laying his hands on the dress of Cora, "the wigwam of the Huron is still open. Will the dark-hair go to Magua's tribe?"

"Never! Strike, and complete your revenge."

He hesitated a moment, and then taking Alice in his arms, the Indian moved swiftly toward the woods.

"Hold!" shrieked Cora, following wildly in his footsteps. "Free the child!"

But Magua knew his power.

"Stay, lady — stay," called Gamut.

David followed the sister, raising his voice in sacred song. In this manner, they crossed the plain. Cora would have fallen under the blows of her enemies, but the strange man who followed her seemed mad to the natives, and that protected them.

Magua entered the woods, where horses awaited him. They mounted and rushed deeper into the forest. David threw his long leg across the saddle of a beast they had left and followed.

They soon began to climb. When they reached the mountaintop, Magua allowed them to dismount, and they saw the sickening sight below.

The cruel work continued while the French columns *stood by*. Finally, the shrieks of the wounded and the yells of the murderers quieted.

Chapter XVIII

The third day after the capture of the fort, about an hour before the setting of the sun, five men moved from the trees. The Mohicans and the scout, together with Munro and Heyward, moved slowly among the horrors of the spot. The father was in search of his children.

When Uncas, who moved in front, had reached the center of the plain, he raised a cry. The young warrior had halted over a group of females who lay in a confused pile of dead. Munro and Heyward flew toward the pile, trying to discover whether those they sought were among the bodies. The father and lover found instant comfort in the search. The scout approached.

"I have been on many a shocking field," he said, "but never has the hand of the devil been so plain!"

"Hugh!" exclaimed Uncas, springing away from the spot. In the next instant, he tore from a bush a piece of the green riding scarf of Cora.

"My child!" said Munro. "Give me my child!"

"Uncas will try," was the short answer.

"Uncas, you are right," returned the scout. "The dark-hair has been here, and she has escaped to the wood. Let us search for the marks she left."

The young Mohican soon raised a cry of success from the edge of the forest. On reaching the spot, the anxious party saw another piece of the scarf.

"Hugh!" exclaimed Chingachgook, who had been examining the low bushes. He now pointed downward.

"Here is the clear print of the footstep of a man!" cried Heyward. "They are captives."

Uncas examined the print. At last he stood.

"The Sly Fox!"

"Ha! That devil again! Here then have passed the dark-hair and Magua. Of Alice we have not yet seen the signs," returned the scout, looking around. "Uncas, bring here the thing you see hanging from that bush."

The scout received the prize and laughed. " 'Tis the whistle of the singer! Now we shall have a wide trail to follow. We know that the Huron has passed, and the dark-hair, and the singer, but where is she of the yellow hair and blue eyes? Move on, Uncas, and keep your eyes on the dried leaves. I will watch the bushes while your father shall run with a *nose to the ground*. Move on, friends. The sun is getting behind the hills."

Before long the Indians stopped and gazed at some signs on the earth.

"Here have been horses!" exclaimed the scout.

"Now the whole secret is out. There they mounted the beasts, and there runs the clear path to Canada."

"But still there are no signs of Alice," said Duncan.

"Perhaps the shining jewel Uncas has just lifted from the ground is one. Pass it this way, Uncas, that we may look at it."

Heyward instantly knew it was a piece of jewelry that Alice had worn on the morning of the massacre. He seized it and pressed it against his heart.

"We should not delay our march," said Heyward.

"We are not *about to* start on a squirrel hunt, but to move for days and nights across a wilderness where men seldom go. We will go back and light our fire tonight in the ruins of the old fort, and in the morning we shall be fresh and ready to attempt our work like men, and not like eager boys."

Heyward saw that argument with the scout was useless. The young man took Munro by the arm and followed in the footsteps of the Indians and the scout, who had already begun to return to the plain.

Chapter XIX

Evening had come when the party entered the ruins of William Henry. Uncas placed a few logs against a blackened wall, and when he had covered them with branches, he pointed toward his rough shelter. Heyward understood the meaning of the gesture and gently aided Munro to enter.

Hawkeye and the Indians lighted a fire and took their evening meal of dried bear's meat. Duncan visited the side of the fort that looked out on the Horican. He stood for many minutes, looking into the night where the dead lay. He soon thought he heard strange sounds from the place. Then swift footsteps seemed to rush across the darkness. Duncan spoke in a low voice to the scout, asking him to come to him.

"Listen," said Duncan, "there are noises on the plain. You hear them?"

"Aye, aye. When food is low and when food is plenty, a wolf grows bold," said the scout.

Duncan now understood the noises he had heard, and spoke with the scout for a few minutes.

"What goes there?" then said the scout.

"Is it not the rushing of the wolves?"

Hawkeye slowly shook his head and moved to a spot away from the light of the fire.

"We must give a call to Uncas."

The young Mohican sprang to his feet as he heard the moaning of an owl. In a few moments Uncas moved cautiously to the spot where they stood.

Hawkeye explained his wishes in a few words. Uncas threw himself on the ground and vanished.

"Chingachgook sits by the light of that fire, and he will become the first and most certain victim," said Heyward.

"You speak the truth," returned the scout. He put his fingers to his mouth and made a low hissing sound like a snake. The moment he heard the warning, Chingachgook seemed to sink, like a man who plans to rest. He changed his position, and then waited. But there was no attack. After a pause, they heard a splash in the water and the report of a rifle.

"There goes Uncas!" said the scout.

"What can this mean?" demanded Duncan.

Just then Uncas returned to the circle and seated himself at the fire.

"What has become of our enemy, Uncas?" demanded Duncan. "We heard your rifle and hoped you had not fired *in vain*."

The young chief removed a fold of his hunting shirt and quietly exposed the tuft of hair which he carried as the symbol of victory.

"Is it a party, or only one?" asked the scout.

Uncas held up a finger and said, "One."

After a short pause, Chingachgook lighted a pipe and began smoking. He then passed the pipe to the scout. The pipe made its rounds three times in silence. Then the chief, as the oldest, began to speak. The scout answered him, and Chingachgook replied. Heyward understood that the Indians desired a pursuit by land, while Hawkeye wanted to cross the lake.

Hawkeye spoke of the age and weakness of Munro. He imitated the light and graceful movements of a canoe, in contrast to the uncertain steps of a tired, old man. He ended by pointing to the scalp of the dead Indian and spoke of the need of leaving speedily, and in a way that would leave no trail.

The Mohicans listened gravely and changed their own opinions to follow his way of thinking. Then they abruptly stretched their forms and closed their eyes in sleep.

Heyward soon imitated their example, and they, who lay in the ruined fort, seemed to slumber as heavily as the bones on the surrounding plain.

Chapter XX

The sky was still star-filled when Hawkeye awakened the sleepers and whispered to Munro and Heyward:

"Speak not a word. Come, and be careful to step on the stones and pieces of wood as you go."

His companions obeyed, and with care they climbed after the scout until they reached the sandy shore of the Horican. There he laid a board from the ruins to the canoe which Uncas brought close to land, and made a sign for the two officers to enter. Then Hawkeye put everything the way it had been and succeeded in reaching the little boat without leaving any marks. Heyward was silent until the Indians had cautiously paddled the canoe some distance from the fort. Then he demanded:

"Why did we leave hurriedly and secretly?"

"Have you forgotten the reptile that Uncas killed?"

"No. But he was alone."

"Aye, but his tribe has many warriors, and others may tell of his death. I have put a trail of water between us."

"With foes in front and foes in our rear, our journey may be one of danger."

"Not really danger, but we shall have to push forward, and perhaps fight," said Hawkeye calmly.

Heyward sat in silence while the canoe glided over several miles of water. Just as the day dawned, they entered the narrow part of the lake and moved swiftly and cautiously among many little islands.

Chingachgook made a light tap on the side of the canoe to warn them of danger. The Indian raised his paddle and pointed.

"I see nothing," said Duncan.

"Hist," interrupted the scout. "You see the smoke that is rising above the island? 'Tis from a fire. We must make a push, and if the Indians or Frenchers are in the narrows, run through."

They used their paddles energetically, and in a few moments they saw two canoes and a fire.

"Together, friends — we are nearly out of reach of a bullet."

The crack of a rifle and a yell from the island interrupted his speech. In another instant, several savages rushed into the canoes and were soon rushing over the water in pursuit.

"Turn her a little more from the sun, Chingachgook, and we will put the island between us."

A long, low island lay at a little distance before them, and the chasing canoe had to pass on the opposite side to that which the scout and his friends took. When the two canoes came round the island, the fugitives had taken the lead.

"They are preparing for a shot," said Heyward, "and it can't miss."

A volley from the Hurons interrupted him, and the bullets whistled around them. A ball struck the paddle from the hands of the chief and drove it through the air far ahead. A shout rose from the Hurons. As the canoe passed swiftly on, Chingachgook recovered his paddle, and waving it on high, he gave the war whoop of the Mohicans.

Duncan was glad to find that they were moving ahead. In a very few minutes, the scout and the Mohicans had put so much water between them and their enemies that Heyward once more breathed freely.

The lake now widened. They continued for hours until they had reached the northern end of the lake. Here the party landed. Hawkeye and Heyward climbed a nearby hill where Hawkeye pointed out a small black object several miles distant.

" 'Tis a canoe, paddled by our enemies. The moment it is dark, they will be on our trail. We must *throw them off.*"

Hawkeye moved to the shore and spoke to his companions. They then lifted the canoe from the water and carried it on their shoulders into the wood, making as clear a trail as possible. They soon reached a stream, which they crossed, and continued until they came to a large area of rock. From here, they walked backwards on their route to the brook, very carefully. They followed the little stream to the lake and set their canoe on the water again. They paddled along the shore for some distance, covered by some overhanging bushes. Finally, the scout said it would be safe to land.

They waited until evening. Then they pushed silently toward the western shore. They again lifted the boat and carried it into the woods where they hid it carefully under some bushes. The adventurers took their arms and packs and were at last ready to continue.

Chapter XXI

The party had landed in an area between Lake Champlain and the Hudson, Mohawk, and St. Lawrence Rivers. For many hours they traveled, until the scout called a halt for them to pass the night.

The sun was shining in the forest when the travelers continued their journey. After traveling a few miles, Hawkeye became more watchful. He often stopped to examine the trees. He spoke to Chingachgook frequently. At last the scout explained his embarrassment.

"The path of the Hurons has run north, toward Canada. Yet for some time, not a sign of a trail have we crossed! Perhaps we have taken the wrong path."

"God protect us from that mistake!" exclaimed Duncan. "Has Uncas any advice to offer?"

The young Mohican continued to be silent. Chingachgook asked him to speak. Uncas sprang up a short hill and stood over a spot of fresh earth.

" 'Tis the trail!" exclaimed the scout, advancing to the spot.

"Why did he keep quiet so long?" muttered Duncan.

"He would not have spoken without permission. The Indian knows the value of years and respects them," answered Hawkeye.

"See!" said Uncas, pointing north. "The dark-hair has gone toward the snows."

Their advance now was rapid, and by the middle of the afternoon, they had found a place where the party of Magua had halted. While they saw the footsteps of men and beasts, the trail appeared to have suddenly ended.

"The Hurons are gone," said the scout. "Let us then hunt for their path."

Finally Uncas pointed out the print of a moccasin in the moist earth.

"That is not the footstep of an Indian!" said Hawkeye. "I can read it plainly. They forced the singer to go first, and the others have walked in his steps."

The party now followed, keeping anxious eyes on the prints. After more than half a mile, they found the print of a foot.

"Here we have three pair of moccasins, and two of little feet!" cried the delighted Hawkeye.

Cheered by these signs, the party made a short halt for a hurried meal. Then the scout pushed forward rapidly. Before an hour had passed, however, the speed of Hawkeye slowed. He soon stopped again.

"I smell the Hurons," he said. "Chingachgook, you take the hillside to the right, Uncas will move along the brook to the left, and I will try the trail. If anything should happen, give three calls of a crow."

The Indians left without reply while Hawkeye continued with the two gentlemen. The scout asked Heyward to move to the edge of the wood. Duncan obeyed and soon stood in a cleared area. Someone had removed many acres of trees. A short distance ahead, the stream opened into a little lake, covering most of the low land. A hundred earthen dwellings stood on the edge of the lake and even in the water. The houses had rounded roofs, and the town seemed more planned than most Indian villages. It seemed deserted, however. Suddenly, the place came alive with beings that moved swiftly from place to place.

The young man started when he saw he was within a hundred yards of a strange Indian. The native, like himself, seemed busy looking at the village. Duncan could not see his face through the paint. His head was shaved, as usual. Duncan was still observing the person when the scout stole silently to his side.

"The savage appears to have no weapons," said Heyward. "We have little to fear from him, but he must not give the alarm to his friends who are moving about the water."

The scout turned to Heyward and looked at him a moment with amazement. Then he laughed silently.

"Keep him under your rifle while I creep in behind and take him alive. Don't fire," said Hawkeye.

The next moment he disappeared among the leaves. After several minutes, the scout reappeared, creeping along the earth in the rear of the savage. He rose to his feet silently and slowly. At that instant, several loud blows hit the water, and Duncan saw a hundred dark forms dive below. The savage watched with a sort of silly curiosity. In the meantime, the hand of Hawkeye was above him. But then the scout removed it, tapped his victim lightly on the shoulder, and exclaimed:

"Greetings, friend! Are you teaching the beavers to sing?"

"Aye," was the answer. "God gave them power to improve his world and perhaps gave them voices to give him thanks."

Chapter XXII

The surprise of Heyward was great. His Indians became beavers, his lake a beaver pond, and the enemy his friend, David Gamut, the song master.

Hawkeye merrily agreed that the Hurons had disguised Gamut well.

"You wanted to practice your singing among the beavers?" he said. "The animals have no voices!" And he made the call of a crow ring in the air.

"See," continued the scout, as he pointed toward the two approaching Mohicans, "this is music which is useful. But we see that you are safe. Now tell us: what has become of the maidens?"

"They are both captives," said David.

"Bless you for these words!" exclaimed Munro.

"They are still in danger," returned David. "The leader of these savages is evil. He hunts today with his young men, and tomorrow they move on toward Canada. They carried the older maiden to a neighboring people, while the younger is with the Huron women, two miles away."

"Alice, my gentle Alice!" murmured Heyward.

"And why do they permit you to move about unwatched?"

David timidly replied, "The power of my music has its influence even over the savage."

The scout laughed and, tapping his forehead meaningfully, said, "The Indians never harm a madman. But why did you not escape?"

"My feet must follow those tender ones. I cannot take one step backward while they are captives," David answered.

Uncas and his father looked at David with satisfaction.

The scout shook his head and replied, "Here, friend. I did plan to make a fire with this whistle of yours, but since you value the thing, take it!"

Gamut received his whistle with pleasure. Then Heyward and Munro questioned him about their journey and the health of the other captives.

Magua had taken the route along the western side of the Horican toward Canada. They allowed David to travel with them. Magua felt the respect that Indians show to those whom God has made weak-minded. On their arrival at the camp of his people,

49

Magua separated his prisoners. He sent Cora to a tribe in a nearby valley. David knew nothing of their name. He only knew that they had not fought at William Henry, that they were allies of Montcalm, and that they were friendly with Magua's Indians.

"They draw strange pictures in their paint, especially one like a tortoise."

"Hugh!" exclaimed both Mohicans at the same time. Then the father lifted his arm and placed his finger on his chest. Duncan saw a tortoise beautifully worked in blue on the chest of the chief.

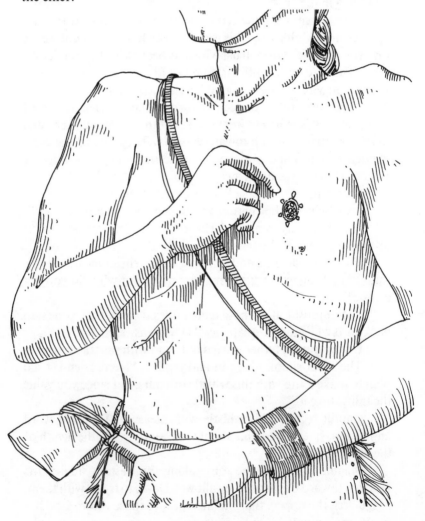

The scout turned and said, "This may be good or evil to us. Chingachgook has noble blood of the Delawares and is the great chief of their Tortoises! We move in a dangerous path. They have a long and sad history, and the white man has done much evil. It has *turned* the tomahawk of brother *against* brother. We must let the singer go in again as usual to give warning to the gentle one of our approach."

"I will go with him," interrupted Heyward.

"You!" exclaimed the astonished Hawkeye. "Are you tired of seeing the sun rise and set?"

"I too can play the madman, the fool. Argue no longer. I have decided."

Hawkeye gazed at the young man a moment in speechless amazement. Duncan continued:

"You have the means of disguise. Change me. Paint me, too. You have heard that the Indians are of two tribes. While you are arranging with your friends for the release of one of the sisters, I will free the other, or die."

"Come," said the scout. "Chingachgook has many different paints. Seat yourself on the log."

Duncan obeyed, and the Mohican quickly drew shadows and lines that changed the warrior to a clown. With his knowledge of French, Duncan might *pass for* an entertainer from Ticonderoga, wandering among the friendly tribes.

When he was ready, the scout told Heyward he planned to leave Munro in some safe camp with Chingachgook while he and Uncas searched among the Delawares.

"And now God bless you!" he continued.

Duncan shook his hand warmly and motioned to David to move on. Hawkeye gazed after him for several moments. Then shaking his head, he turned and led his own party into the forest.

When Duncan found himself alone with the singer, he began to understand the difficulties of his task. Then he pictured Alice and her danger, and he forgot all his own risk.

Within half an hour they reached the edge of an area where Duncan saw fifty or sixty lodges. Together, they continued their way toward the tents.

Chapter XXIII

Duncan and David soon found themselves in the center of a group of children. The whole pack raised a shrill and warning whoop. The cry of the children drew a dozen warriors to the door of the nearest lodge. They stood in a dark and savage group, gravely awaiting the approach of those who had unexpectedly come among them.

David led the way into this very building. Duncan found it difficult to act unafraid as he brushed the dark and powerful frames of the savages. But he trusted to his companion, whose footsteps he closely followed. Within the lodge, imitating the example of Gamut, he seated himself in silence.

Arranging themselves around him, the Indians seemed patiently to wait for the stranger to speak. At last, one whose hair was gray advanced from a corner and spoke. Heyward could not understand his words. He shook his head.

"Do none of my brothers speak French?" he said, looking about him from face to face. "The *heart* of the Great Father *would be heavy* to think that none of this wise and brave nation understand his language."

A long pause followed. At last, the same warrior who had before addressed him replied, "Our Great Father does not reward his Indians when he counts the scalps we took five nights ago. His *ears are open* to the Delawares, who are not our friends."

"It cannot be. See, he has told me, a man that knows the art of healing, to go to his children, the Hurons of the great lakes. He said to help any who are sick!"

Another silence followed Duncan's words. The Indian spoke again.

"Do the men of the Canadas paint their skins? We have heard them boast that their faces were pale."

"When an Indian chief comes among his white fathers," returned Duncan, "he lays aside his buffalo robe to carry the shirt that we offer him. My brothers have given me paint, and I wear it."

A murmur of approval announced that the Indians favorably received the honor to the tribe.

Suddenly a fearful sound rose from the forest, and a high, shrill yell immediately followed it. The sudden and terrible interruption caused Duncan to start from his seat. At the same moment, the warriors glided from the lodge. Duncan broke from the place and stood in the center of a crowd. Men, women, and children were all there, some exclaiming loudly, others clapping their hands with a frantic joy, and all expressing their savage pleasure.

A line of warriors moved from the woods and advanced slowly toward the dwellings. One in front carried a short pole on which hung several human scalps. Heyward knew that a successful war party was returning. The light was not strong, but Heyward could see that in advance of the warriors were two men. One stood tall and firm, while the other bowed his head in terror or shame. Their captors drove them to the center of the village and then to the door of the chief lodge.

The Huron women abused the firm, quiet stranger. The stranger *paid no attention* to the women. He turned his face toward the light and looked at the warriors. The change of position permitted Duncan to look into the firm and sharp eyes of Uncas.

Heyward trembled at the fearful situation of his friend. Just then a warrior motioned the women and children away with a gesture, took Uncas by the arm, and led him into the lodge. All the chiefs followed, and the anxious Heyward entered without attracting attention to himself.

Uncas stood in the center of the lodge, calm and proud. The other Indian whom Duncan had observed sat apart. In the meantime, the older chiefs spoke with each other. The gray-haired chief rose and placed himself in front of this young Huron.

"Reed-that-bends," he said, "your tongue is loud in the village, but in battle it is still. The enemy knows the shape of your back, but they have never seen the color of your eyes. Three times have they called on you to come, and each time you forgot to answer. Your tribe will never again mention your name — we have forgotten it already."

As the chief uttered these words, the young man rose to his feet and looked steadily at the glittering knife that his judge held. As the weapon passed into his heart he even smiled; he seemed to find death less fearful than he had expected. He fell heavily on his face at the feet of Uncas. Then the whole group glided from the lodge, and Duncan thought that he and the dead victim were alone. 54

Chapter XXIV

A moment later a powerful hand grasped his arm, and the low voice of Uncas muttered in his ears, "The grayhead and the Mohican chief are safe, and the rifle of Hawkeye is not asleep. Go."

Heyward mixed with the crowd outside. A group of warriors entered the place again and carried the dead body into the woods. Duncan wandered among the lodges unnoticed, trying to find Alice. He went from tent to tent, looking into each, until he had circled the entire village unsuccessfully. Then he returned to the chief lodge to find David.

The warriors had gathered again and were calmly smoking. Duncan took a seat in the shadows. One of the older warriors addressed him in French.

"An evil spirit lives in the wife of one of my young men. Can the stranger frighten him away?"

"Spirits differ," Heyward answered. "Some surrender to the power of knowledge, while others are too strong."

"My brother is a great medicine," said the clever savage. "He will try?"

Duncan nodded in agreement. The Huron prepared to lead the way to the invalid. Just then, a warrior of powerful frame marched into the lodge and seated himself. Duncan felt his body shiver with horror when he found himself near Magua.

The return of this chief caused a delay in the departure of the Huron. Several Indians lighted pipes again and joined the newcomer in smoking.

"Has my friend found meat?" one said.

"The young men stagger under the weight," returned Magua.

Then one of the chiefs said to Magua, "One of the Delawares has been sneaking around my village," and he pointed to the immovable form of Uncas.

Magua rose to look at the prisoner. Uncas turned to the light, and their eyes met. Magua's expression became one of fierce joy, and he uttered the fearful name:

"The Bounding Elk!"

Magua raised his arm, shook it at the captive, and exclaimed in English:

"Mohican, you die!"

"That will never bring the dead Hurons to life," returned Uncas. "The river washes their bones."

One warrior stood, uttered a yell, and swung his ax above his head. As it spun from his hand, Magua's arm shot forward to ruin its aim. The weapon passed through the wall of the lodge.

"No!" said Magua. "The sun must shine on his shame. The squaws must see him tremble. Go — take him where there is silence. Let us see if a Delaware can sleep at night and, in the morning, die."

The guards tied his arms and led Uncas from the lodge. Magua also left the place. Heyward felt his fear lessen when this dangerous foe left. The chief who had asked the aid of Duncan moved to depart. Duncan was glad to breathe the clear evening air.

Instead of passing among the lodges where Heyward had made his unsuccessful search, his companion moved toward a nearby mountain. The blaze of a fire in the camp lighted the way of the chief and Duncan. In front of a rock, they came to a grassy spot. Just then someone added fresh fuel to the fire, and the light showed a dark and mysterious being in their path.

The Indian paused. Again the fire brightened, and Duncan saw it was a bear. The Huron seemed to think this stranger was peaceable, for he quietly continued on his way.

Duncan knew that Indians often tamed the bear, and he followed his companion, but his nervousness grew when he saw the beast following their footsteps. The Indian at that moment pushed open a door of bark and entered a cave in the mountain.

Duncan stepped after him and was closing the cover to the opening when the shaggy beast drew it back. They were now in a long hallway in the rocks. The young man kept as close as possible to his guide. The bear growled frequently at his heels, and once or twice laid its huge paws on him.

They now arrived at a large place in the rock, which the Indians had divided into many rooms with stones and bark. Openings above let in the light by day, and at night lighted branches supplied light. Here the Hurons had brought the sick woman. Duncan approached her bedside, and among the females surrounding it, Heyward found his friend David.

One look was enough to show Duncan that the invalid was beyond the powers of healing. She lay unmoving, unconscious of suffering.

Gamut began singing, hoping to work a miracle. The Indians respected his imaginary madness and allowed him to finish. As the song ended, Duncan heard it repeated behind him, in a voice half human and half ghostly. Looking around, he saw the shaggy monster seated in a shadow of the cave, where it repeated in a growl something like the song of Gamut.

David's eyes opened wide in wonder. Then he exclaimed to Duncan, "She expects you and is nearby," and he immediately left the cave.

Chapter XXV

The chief sent away the females. When they had left, he said, "Now let my brother show his power."

Heyward prepared to perform chants like an Indian magician. However, the beast interrupted every attempt with a fierce growl.

"The spirits are jealous," said the Huron. "I go. Peace," he said to the beast. "I go."

When the Indian left, the bear came up to Duncan. The huge paws pushed the head to one side, and the honest face of the scout appeared.

"Why do you wear this disguise?" asked Duncan.

"After we separated," returned the scout, "I placed the commandant and Chingachgook safely in an old beaver lodge. Then Uncas and I pushed for the other camp. Have you seen the Mohican?"

"He is captive and will die at sunrise."

"Uncas and I met a party of the Hurons. One of the Hurons was a coward and, in running away, led Uncas into an ambush. That is my reason for being here. I could not leave Uncas to the Hurons. I was near to the lodges and luck led me to their magician, who was dressing himself. A hit over the head made him unconscious for a time and I borrowed his skins. But where is Alice? You heard the singer as he left us. Here are walls. A bear should climb; therefore, will I take a look above them."

The scout climbed the wall and slid down again.

"She is here," he whispered. "By that door you will find her."

Duncan found Alice in another apartment, anxious and terrified. David had prepared her for his visit.

"Duncan!" she exclaimed in a trembling voice.

Duncan told her the events we have followed.

"And now, Alice," he added, "with the aid of our friend, the scout, we may find our way from this place, but you will have to be very brave." The young man was about to continue when a tap on his shoulder interrupted him. Starting to his feet, he turned and looked on the evil face of Magua.

Magua closed the door by which he had entered. Then he spoke to his prisoners. "How brave is the white man at the stake? The Sly Fox will go and bring his young men. Can a paleface laugh at torture?"

He turned away to leave the place when the bear appeared in the door. Magua recognized the well-known costume of the magician and prepared to pass it. Suddenly the beast reached out and grasped him in a "bear hug." Heyward picked up some deerskin and tied Magua's arms, legs, and feet. Then they laid their helpless enemy on his back.

Hawkeye removed the jaws of the beast, showed his face, and immediately gagged his enemy's mouth.

"Bring on the gentle one," said the scout. "Wrap her in those Indian clothes. Cover all of her. Now take her in your arms and follow."

Duncan eagerly obeyed and followed the scout to the entrance. As they approached the door of bark, a murmur of voices told them that the friends and relatives of the invalid were gathered outside.

"If I speak," Hawkeye whispered, "my English will tell them that an enemy is among them. You must say that we have shut the evil spirit in the cave, and are taking the woman to the woods to find strengthening roots."

The scout boldly left the place, acting like a bear. The father approached.

"Has my brother driven away the evil spirit?" he demanded. "What has he in his arms?"

"The child," returned Duncan gravely. "The disease has gone out of her; it is shut up in the rocks. I take the woman to strengthen her against further attacks."

The father explained the stranger's words, and a murmur of satisfaction rose among the Indians. The chief waved his hand for Duncan to go on, saying, "Go. I will enter the rock and fight the wicked one."

"Is my brother mad?" exclaimed Heyward. "He will meet the disease, and it will enter him, or he will drive out the disease, and it will chase his daughter into the woods. Wait here, and if the spirit appears, beat him with clubs."

The Indians agreed, and the magicians left. When they were at a distance from the lodges, Hawkeye made a halt and spoke.

"Follow this path until you come to a fall. Climb the hill on your right, and you will see fires. There you must go and demand protection; if they are true Delawares, you will be safe."

"And you!" demanded Heyward, in surprise. "Surely we shall not separate here?"

"The Hurons hold the last of the high blood of the Mohicans," returned the scout. "I go to help him. If he goes to the stake, I shall die with him."

Duncan and Alice begged that he would avoid the danger. The scout listened and then spoke.

"You have risked life and all that is dear to you to rescue this gentle one. I have fought beside Uncas in many a bloody battle. Winters and summers, nights and days, we have traveled the wilderness together, and that Mohican boy shall not die alone!"

The scout turned toward the lodges, and Heyward and Alice went toward the village of the Delawares.

Chapter XXVI

Hawkeye returned to the camp. As he approached the lodges, he noticed a tent apart from the others. There the scout went.

David Gamut sat before a low fire. Hawkeye moved into the lodge and seated himself.

"Dark and mysterious monster!" David exclaimed, while his hands trembled. "I know not your plans, but listen to the sacred language of the Psalms."

A well-known voice replied, "Put up the whistling weapon, and give me some words of English now."

"What are you?" gasped David.

"A man like yourself," returned Hawkeye, removing his bear head. "Now let us to business. Can you lead me to Uncas?"

"The task will not be difficult," returned David.

"Lead on," replied Hawkeye, covering his face.

Uncas was in a lodge in the center of the village. Four or five guards were about the door of the prison. At the sight of David, who had become friendly with one of the guards, and their well-known magician, they readily *made way*. The scout could not address the Hurons in their own language and had to trust the conversation entirely to David.

"Does my brother wish to see The Bounding Elk weep before the Hurons tomorrow? Then let him step aside, and this man will blow upon the dog!"

The Huron explained the words of David to the others, who listened and motioned them to enter.

The scout slowly entered. Uncas was in a corner, hands and feet tied. He did not glance at the animal, but when he heard a low hissing sound, he looked about him. He heard the sound repeated, coming from the mouth of the beast. Uncas uttered, "Hawkeye!"

"Cut his ropes," said Hawkeye to David.

David did so. The scout dropped the animal skin and rose to his feet. He gave a long knife to Uncas, at the same time keeping one for himself.

"We will go to the Tortoises," said Uncas. "They are the children of my grandfathers."

"Aye," returned Hawkeye. "Put on the skin; you can play the bear. Now, friend," said Hawkeye to David, "an exchange of clothes will be a great help. Here, take my hunting shirt and cap, and give me your blanket and hat and book. If we ever meet again, you shall have all back again, with many thanks."

David parted with the objects readily. When Hawkeye dressed in his borrowed clothes, he might have passed for the singer by starlight. The scout gave David parting instructions.

"Your chief danger will be when the savages find out the trick. If they don't kill you then, you will be safe in your madness. If you stay, you must sit in the shadow and act the part of Uncas until the Indians discover the lie. Choose yourself — to make a rush or stay here."

"I will stay," said David. "He has battled for me bravely, and this I will dare for him."

"God bless you, friend."

The scout immediately left the lodge, with the new beast. Hawkeye began an imitation of David's singing. The Hurons stopped the 'singing master.'

"The Mohican dog! Is he afraid? Will the Hurons hear him weep?"

A growl so fierce and natural came from the beast that the Indians moved aside. Hawkeye *broke out* into song. The group of Indians drew back and allowed the magician and his assistant to leave.

Uncas and the scout continued past the lodges. When they were out of the village, a loud cry rose from the lodge. The Mohican shook off his shaggy covering. The scout tore two rifles from beneath a bush. Then they bounded forward and were soon hidden in the darkness of the forest.

Chapter XXVII

The impatience of the savages about the prison of Uncas had conquered their fear. They moved cautiously to a crack and looked through. For several minutes they mistook David for their prisoner. But when David, unconscious of the watchers, turned his head and exposed his face, they immediately discovered the trick. They rushed together into the lodge and laid their hands on their captive. David thought his final hour had come. He broke out in a loud funeral song. This reminded the Indians of his madness, and rushing into the open air, they aroused the village.

Immediately two hundred men rose and crowded around the chief lodge. All looked for Magua, surprised that he did not appear. Several warriors approached, bringing with them the unfortunate magician whom Hawkeye had left in the woods. All listened to his story, and when he had finished, the father of the sick woman stepped forward and told his tale. A few of the chiefs went to the cave.

The outer room was silent and dark. The woman lay in her usual place, yet some present said they had seen the paleface carry her to the woods. The father went to the bed and looked at his daughter. She was dead.

Then a dark-looking object rolled out of the next room into the very center of the room where they stood. The whole party drew back a little, until they recognized the fierce features of Magua.

Several ready knives released his arms and legs. The Huron rose. His hand played with the handle of his knife.

"Let the Mohican die!" exclaimed Magua, in a voice of thunder.

The oldest of the party said, "He is swift and leaps far, but my young men are on his trail."

"Is he gone?" demanded Magua.

"An evil spirit has been among us."

"An evil spirit!" repeated the other angrily. " 'Tis the spirit that has taken the lives of so many Hurons, that killed my young men at the falling river, and who has now tied the arms of The Sly Fox! The dog who wears a pale skin — The Long Rifle."

That name produced a fearful rage among his hearers.

"My people wait," Magua said. "Let us go."

The whole party returned to the chief lodge. When they were seated, all eyes turned to Magua. He rose and told his tale and then laid his plans before his tribe. He sent spies to approach and study the camp of the Delawares, for he knew they would go there. He sent the warriors to their lodges. Then Magua retired to his own lodge where he sat, thinking of his future plans.

Long before the day dawned, warrior after warrior entered the lodge of Magua until they numbered twenty. Each carried his rifle, yet the paint was peaceful. Then Magua rose and gave the signal to follow. They slipped from their camp unobserved.

Magua led his party along the little lake of the beavers. One chief carried the beaver as his symbol, or "totem." This man paused and spoke friendly words to the beavers. He spoke of their present march and asked the beavers to give him wisdom.

Just as he ended his speech, the head of a large beaver showed from the door of a lodge. The Indian took this as a favorable sign and offered his thanks.

The Indians moved away, and the animal watched their movements. As the party entered the forest, the entire animal came out of the lodge, uncovering the features of Chingachgook from his mask of fur.

Chapter XXVIII

Later that morning, a man suddenly appeared at the edge of the Delaware camp. He carried no arms, and his paint was peaceful. He made a friendly gesture. The villagers answered his salute by a murmur of welcome. The dark figure moved with dignity into the center of the camp. He made many signs of greeting to the men he passed. When he reached their chiefs, the Delawares saw that the well-known Huron chief, The Sly Fox, stood before them.

"The wise Huron is welcome," said the leading chief. He stretched out his arm, and they exchanged friendly greetings. Then the Delaware invited his guest to enter his own lodge and share his morning meal. Magua accepted the invitation. When both had eaten, Magua spoke.

"Does my prisoner give trouble to my brothers?"

"She is welcome."

"Send her to my squaws if she gives trouble."

"She is welcome," returned the chief again.

Magua continued silent several minutes after his unsuccessful effort to recover possession of Cora.

"Have there been strange moccasins in the woods? Has my brother smelled white men?"

"There have been strange moccasins about my camp. The stranger is always welcome in my lodges."

"The stranger, but not the spy. When our Canada father hears that his greatest enemy eats in your camp and smokes at your fire, he will think you have turned from him. Does the paleface who has murdered so many of his friends go in and out among the Delawares?"

"Who has murdered my young men? Who is the enemy of my Great Father?"

"The Long Rifle."

"What does my brother mean?" demanded the chief.

"Let the Delawares count their prisoners."

The chief sent messengers to call a solemn meeting of the nation.

In half an hour each individual, including even the women and children, was in place. There were more than a thousand people. They waited for the oldest and most experienced of the men to lead the council.

67

At last, the whole nation rose to their feet. Three men slowly approached the place. They were all old, but one in the center, who leaned on his companion for support, had lived more than a century. He struggled slowly over the ground. His dark, wrinkled face contrasted with his long white hair. His robe was of the finest skins. Silver covered his tomahawk, and the handle of his knife shone with gold.

The crowd hummed with pleasure when he appeared, and then whispered the name of "Tamenund" from mouth to mouth. Magua had often heard of this wise and just Delaware. Therefore, he eagerly stepped out a little from the crowd to catch a nearer look at the man whose decision would influence his own future.

The eyes of the old man were closed. Perhaps they were tired of seeing the selfishness of humans. He passed Magua without notice and moved to the center of his nation where he sat with the dignity of a monarch and the manner of a father.

After a short delay, a few of the young men rose, left the crowd, and entered a nearby lodge. In a few minutes they reappeared, escorting some individuals toward the seat of judgment.

Chapter XXIX

Cora stood before the chief, holding Alice in her arms. At their side stood Heyward. Hawkeye was a little in the rear. Uncas was not there.

One of the old chiefs demanded in English, "Which of my prisoners is The Long Rifle?"

Duncan had glanced around and had seen Magua. He knew at once that the savage had some plan against them, and he decided to try to block his plans.

"Give us weapons," he boldly replied, "and our actions shall speak for us!"

The scout now moved to the front and said, "My family named me Nathaniel; the Delawares, Hawkeye; and the Hurons, The Long Rifle."

"My brother has said that a snake crept into my camp," said the chief to Magua. "Which is he?"

The Huron pointed to the scout.

"When did a wolf speak the truth?" said Duncan.

"Give my prisoners guns," said the chief, "and let them prove the truth."

The friendly opponents immediately received weapons and had to fire at a clay pot which lay on a stump. Raising his rifle with care, Heyward fired. The bullet cut the wood within a few inches of the pot, and the Indians knew that the shot showed skill.

The scout raised his rifle and shook it at Magua.

"Huron, I could shoot you now, did I choose to send a bullet to your heart! Yet I might draw down evil on tender and innocent heads." The scout dropped his weapon, and it fired, scattering pieces of the pot into the air.

"It was an accident!" Heyward exclaimed. "None can shoot without aiming!"

"Accident!" cried the scout. "You see the clay pot hanging from that tree? Let me see you break it!"

Duncan aimed carefully. He fired, and three or four young Indians sprang forward and announced that the bullet was in the tree, next to the object.

"I hope the squaw who owns the pot has more of them in her wigwam," said Hawkeye, laughing, "for this will never hold water again!"

The scout slowly raised his rifle, held it level for a moment, and fired. The young Indians announced that they could find no trace of the bullet.

"If you would find the bullet of a sharpshooter," returned Hawkeye, "you must look *in* the object and not around it!"

The Indians tore the pot from the tree and held it high with a shout, showing a hole in the bottom which the bullet had cut after passing through the opening in the center. A loud expression of wonder burst from the mouth of every warrior.

"Brother," said the chief, turning to Magua, "what brings the Huron here?"

"Justice. His prisoners are with his brothers, and he comes for his own."

Tamenund said, "Justice is the law. Take them."

Four or five warriors stepped behind Heyward and the scout and tied their arms rapidly. Magua threw a look of triumph at Cora. Then he took Alice from the arms of the warrior who held her and began to leave. But Cora rushed to the feet of the chief and cried:

"Just and honorable Delaware, on your wisdom and power we lean for mercy! Be deaf to that monster, who lies to feed his thirst for blood."

The chief gazed at Cora and said, "Who are you?"

"A woman who has never harmed you. We are captives who ask only permission to leave in peace. There is one of your own people who has not come before you. Hear him speak before the Huron leaves in triumph, Father of these people."

Tamenund questioned his companions, who said, "It is a snake — a redskin in the pay of the palefaces. We keep him for torture."

"Let him come," returned the chief.

The young men obeyed his order.

Chapter XXX

After a few minutes, the crowd opened and shut again, and Uncas stood in the circle. The young Mohican looked about him, and when he saw Tamenund, he advanced and placed himself before the chief.

"What language does the prisoner speak?" demanded the chief.

"Like his fathers," Uncas replied, "with the tongue of a Delaware."

"A Delaware!" repeated the old man. "Never have I known a Delaware to creep, like a poisonous snake, into the camp of his nation. Delaware!" continued the chief. "You are not worthy of the name. The warrior who deserts his tribe is a traitor. The law is just. He is yours, my children. Take him."

A cry burst from the entire nation. A chief announced that the captive must suffer torture by fire. Uncas stood firmly to meet his captors. One of them seized the hunting shirt of the young warrior and tore it from his body. Then he prepared to lead him to the stake. But the savage stopped suddenly and froze in amazement. He pointed to the captive's chest. Every eye stared at the figure of a small tortoise worked on the chest of the prisoner.

71

Uncas smiled calmly. Then he spoke.

"Men of this nation!" he said. "My people hold up the earth! My tribe is the grandfather of nations!"

"Who are you?" demanded Tamenund, rising.

"Uncas, the son of Chingachgook," answered the captive, bowing his head in respect to the other's years, " a son of the great Turtle."

"I thank the Great Spirit that one is here to fill my place at the council fire. Uncas! Let the eyes of a dying eagle gaze on the rising sun."

Tamenund held Uncas and gazed into his face.

"We knew that two warriors of our people were in the hills of the white men. Why have their seats at the councils of the Delawares been so long empty?"

"Once we slept where we could hear the salt lake speak," replied Uncas. "But when we saw a paleface on every brook, we followed the deer back to the river. The Delawares were gone. Then said my father, 'Here will we hunt. The waters of the river go into the salt lake.' The children of the Turtle watch the rising, and not the setting, sun."

The men of the tribe listened to his words with respect. Uncas looked over the crowd and saw Hawkeye. He moved to the side of his friend, cut him free with his own knife, took the scout by the hand, and led him to the feet of the chief.

"Father," he said, "look at this paleface: a just man, and the friend of the Delawares."

"My son has not done well to call him friend," said Tamenund. "He has killed my young men."

"I have killed the Huron," said the scout, "but my hand has never harmed a Delaware knowingly. I am friendly to them and all their nation."

"Where is the Huron?" demanded Tamenund.

Magua, whose feelings the reader may imagine, stepped boldly in front of the chief.

"The just Tamenund," he said, "will not keep what a Huron has lent."

"Tell me, my brother," the chief asked Uncas, "has the stranger a conqueror's right over you?"

"He has none."

"The Long Rifle?"

"Laughs at the Hurons."

"The stranger and the white maiden that came into camp together?"

"Should journey on an open path."

"And the woman that the Huron left with my warriors?"

Uncas made no reply.

"She is mine," cried Magua. "You know it is so."

"My son is silent," said Tamenund.

"It is so," was the low answer.

The chief said, "Huron, go with your own."

"Hold!" cried Duncan, springing forward. "Huron, have mercy! Her ransom shall make you rich."

"Magua wants not money. He has his revenge!"

"To you, just Tamenund, I beg for mercy," exclaimed Heyward.

"The Delaware has spoken," said the chief, closing his eyes. "Men speak not twice."

"Huron," said Hawkeye. "Do you prefer taking that prisoner into your camp, or me?"

"Will The Long Rifle give his life for the woman?" demanded Magua.

"Release the woman. I am your prisoner."

A murmur of approval ran through the crowd. Magua paused. Then, looking at Cora, he said, "The Sly Fox is a great chief; he has but one mind. Come," he added to his captive, "we will go."

"Generous hunter," Cora said to the scout, "from my heart I thank you." After kissing her sister, she said to the savage, "Now, sir, I will follow."

"Huron," said Uncas, "look at the sun. When he rises above the trees, men will be on your trail."

"Send your arrows and your guns," exclaimed Magua, with a laugh. "Dogs — I spit on you."

The triumphant Magua passed into the forest. Cora followed him, and Indian law protected him.

Chapter XXXI

Uncas kept his eyes on Cora until the colors of her dress mixed with the foliage of the forest. Then he disappeared into the lodge from which he had come. A few warriors who had seen the anger in his eyes followed him to the place.

A young warrior at last came from the lodge of Uncas. Moving toward a dwarf pine that grew from a rock, he tore the bark from its body and then returned to the lodge. Soon another followed, who ripped the branches from the tree, leaving it a naked trunk. A third colored the post with stripes of dark red paint. Finally, the Mohican himself reappeared. He was naked except for his belt and leggings, and he had painted one half of his fine features black.

Uncas moved toward the post. He circled it, raising his voice at the same time in his war chant. Warrior after warrior followed his example until all had joined the dance. Then Uncas struck his tomahawk deep into the post and raised his voice in a shout. At this signal, a hundred warriors rushed on the emblem of their enemy and cut it apart, piece by piece, until nothing remained of the trunk but its roots.

The instant Uncas had struck the blow, he moved out of the circle and watched the sun. When it rose above the trees, the truce with Magua would end. Uncas announced that fact with a cry, and the whole crowd prepared for battle.

Uncas now named the chiefs to different responsibilities, and he gave the word to march. More than two hundred men silently obeyed him.

Their entrance into the forest was uneventful. After a few minutes, they saw, from their cover, one person advancing quickly from the side of the enemy. The stranger hesitated, appeared uncertain, and finally halted.

"Hawkeye," said the young chief in a low voice, "he must never speak to the Hurons again."

The scout took careful aim. But, instead of pulling the trigger, he lowered the gun and said, "It is Gamut. I'll have a talk with him."

Hawkeye crawled through the bushes close to David and called softly. The poor fellow appeared relieved.

"The savages are about in great numbers," said David, "and I fear they plan evil."

"Where are the Hurons?" asked the scout.

"They are hiding in the forest between this spot and their village."

Uncas said, "Magua?"

"He brought in the maiden and left her in the cave. He is at the head of his savages."

"He has left her in the cave!" interrupted Heyward. "May we do something for her?"

Uncas looked at the scout and asked, "What says Hawkeye?"

"Give me twenty rifles, and I will turn along the stream and join Chingachgook and the colonel. You shall hear the whoop from there. Then, Uncas, you drive in their front. When they come close enough to our guns, we will give them a blow that shall weaken their line. After that, we will take their village and release the woman from the cave."

Uncas explained the plan to his leaders. They agreed on signals and then separated, each to his task.

Chapter XXXII

Hawkeye led his little group toward the brook. They moved cautiously and reached the point where the little stream joined a larger one.

"Here is an end of our cover," said the scout to Heyward. "The beavers have taken the trees for their food and their dams."

The scout knew that the Huron camp lay a half mile up the brook, and he felt troubled because he had not seen any trace of his enemy. He listened, but he heard nothing but the sighing of the wind. At last, he decided to move cautiously up the stream.

The party had just begun to move when a volley from a dozen rifles broke out, and a Delaware fell dead.

"To cover, men!" shouted Hawkeye.

The contest grew warm. Hawkeye saw his enemy moving men to the side and thought the whole enemy tribe was gradually encircling them. At this moment, they heard the sound of arms from the group with Uncas. The enemy had left too small a force to fight the young Mohican, and the battle now moved toward the village, as many rushed to fight the force of Uncas.

Hawkeye called to his Indians, and the Delawares sprang upon their enemies with fury. The enemy gave up ground until they reached a thicket. At this moment, the crack of a rifle sounded, and a bullet came whistling from among some beaver lodges.

"There speaks Chingachgook!" shouted Hawkeye. "We have them now front and back!"

The Huron warriors *broke off* the fight, thinking only of flight. Many fell under the bullets and the blows of the pursuing Delawares.

Hawkeye led the party to level ground with trees to hide them. Beneath their eyes stretched a narrow wood. Through this dark forest Uncas was still fighting with the main body of the Hurons.

At that instant, Uncas broke from the forest at the head of a hundred warriors. The young chief's followers pursued the enemy into the woods. One group of Hurons had not sought cover and was moving slowly up the hill. Magua led this party.

The moment Uncas saw the figure of The Sly Fox, he rushed upon his enemy. The Long Rifle gave a shout and rushed forward with his companions. The Huron instantly turned and retreated rapidly up the hill.

Uncas continued the pursuit. Both pursuers and pursued entered the village, and the Hurons now fought around their lodges with fury. The tomahawk of Uncas, the blows of Hawkeye, and even the arm of Munro were all busy, and quickly covered the ground with their enemies. Still Magua escaped. He rushed away from the place with two friends.

Uncas bounded forward in pursuit. Magua leaped into a thicket of bushes and entered the cave.

Still Uncas kept his eye on Magua. Heyward and the scout followed, but their way was becoming difficult in the dark tunnels. Suddenly they saw a white robe at the farthest end of a tunnel that seemed to lead up the mountain.

" 'Tis Cora!" exclaimed Heyward, with horror.

"Cora! Cora!" repeated Uncas.

"Courage, lady; we come!" shouted the scout.

The way was rough, broken, and in spots, nearly impassable. Uncas abandoned his rifle. Heyward imitated his example. Both knew its madness a moment later, when the Hurons fired down the tunnel and gave the Mohican a slight wound.

"We must move closer!" said the scout. "They will *pick us off*. See, they use the maiden as protection!"

Uncas took the lead and climbed swiftly. Carrying Cora, the Hurons were *losing ground* in the race.

"Stay, dog!" exclaimed Uncas, shaking his tomahawk at Magua. He saw Magua break out of the tunnel and step out onto the side of the mountain.

"I will go no further," cried Cora, breaking free and stopping on a ledge of rocks that hung over a deep precipice. "Kill me if you will. I will go no further."

The companions of Magua raised their tomahawks, but Magua stopped their arms. He drew his knife and turned to his captive.

"Woman," he said, "choose: the wigwam or the knife of The Sly Fox!"

Cora paid no attention, but dropped to her knees and raised her eyes toward heaven.

The Huron raised his arm, but dropped it again with a bewildered look. He lifted the weapon again — but just then they heard a sharp cry above them, and Uncas appeared, leaping from a fearful height, upon the ledge. Magua stepped back, and one of his assistants *buried his* own *knife* in the chest of Cora.

The Huron sprang on his countryman, but the falling form of Uncas separated them. Maddened by the murder, Magua buried his weapon in the back of the fallen Delaware. But Uncas rose and struck down the murderer of Cora with the last of his strength. The Sly Fox seized the dying Delaware and passed his knife into his chest three times before Uncas fell dead at his feet.

Magua uttered a fierce, wild cry of triumph. The scout just then reached the scene, but he saw only the dead on the ledge.

He looked at the victims and then glanced around. Magua stepped from behind a rock, leaped a wide opening, and climbed the rocks. The Huron shouted, "The palefaces are dogs! The Delawares are women! Magua leaves them on the rocks for the crows!"

He made a desperate leap across the rocks. He *fell short*, but his hands grasped a shrub on the edge of the precipice. Hawkeye crouched, and his body trembled so violently that his rifle moved like a leaf in the wind. Magua rested his feet on a rock. Then he succeeded in drawing his knees to the edge of the mountain. The scout steadied himself and drew the weapon to his shoulder. It poured out its power. The arms of the Huron relaxed, his body fell back a little, his hold loosened, and his dark form cut the air in its rapid flight to destruction.

Chapter XXXIII

The sun found the Delawares the following day a nation of mourners. The battle was over, and they had destroyed the Huron camp.

Still, the Delawares gave no shouts of success, sang no songs of victory. All the living had collected in deep and awful silence.

Six Delaware girls spread sweet-smelling herbs and flowers on a litter that held, under Indian robes, all that remained of the beautiful Cora. At her feet sat the saddened Munro, his aged head bowed nearly to the earth. Gamut stood at his side, his head uncovered. Heyward was also nearby, leaning against a tree trying to control his sorrow.

Another group filled the opposite side of the same area. Uncas was dressed in beautiful clothes. In front of the body sat Chingachgook, without arms, paint, or decoration of any sort. The Mohican warrior gazed at the cold face of his son.

The scout was nearby, leaning on his gun, while Tamenund sat in a high place, looking down on his silent and sorrowful people.

One of the chiefs gave a signal to the women. The girls raised the litter of Cora and advanced with slow steps, chanting as they moved. Munro followed. His friends joined him in the procession. The girls reached a little hill and placed the body in a covering of bark. After that they lowered it into its dark and final home. Then they stood aside.

David poured out his feeling in song while the females listened in sorrow. When he ended his singing, there was a solemn stillness. Then Munro asked the scout to thank the girls for their kindness.

A group of young Indians approached with a covered litter and pointed upward toward the sun.

"I understand you," returned Munro. "Gentlemen," he added, looking about him, "our duty here is over. Let us depart."

Heyward gladly obeyed. He pressed the hand of the scout, threw himself into the saddle, and guided his horse to the side of the litter. The sound of weeping announced the presence of Alice within. In this manner all the white men except Hawkeye passed from the Delaware camp and soon disappeared in the forest.

Hawkeye returned to the camp to catch a parting look at Uncas, whom the Delawares were enclosing in animal skins. Then came a procession like the other, and the whole nation collected about the grave of the young chief.

The body faced the rising sun with the tools of war and of the hunt *at hand*, ready for the final journey. Chingachgook spoke:

"Why do my brothers mourn?" he said. "Why do my daughters weep? A young man has gone to the *happy hunting ground*. A chief has filled his time with honor. He was good, he was dutiful, he was brave. The Great Spirit needs such a warrior, and he has called him away. As for me, I am alone — "

"No!" cried Hawkeye. "Not alone. The boy has left us for a time, but, Chingachgook, you are not alone."

Chingachgook grasped the hand that the scout had stretched out, and these two strong woodsmen bowed their heads together while hot tears fell to their feet, watering the grave of Uncas.

In the awful stillness, Tamenund lifted his voice to send the crowd away.

"It is enough," he said. "Go, children. My day has been too long. In the morning I saw my sons happy and strong, and yet, before the night has come, I have lived to see the last warrior of the wise tribe of the Mohicans."

Glossary

A

abandon (ə ban'dən) v., to leave without planning to return. (9)
The mother cat *abandoned* her kittens.
about (one's) ears (I), in ruin; defeat. (15)
His father's death brought Kevin's plans for college down *about his ears.*
about to (I), ready to; close to. (18)
We were *about to* leave when the rain began.
abrupt (ə brupt') adj., steep; sudden; unexpected. (7)
We climbed down the *abrupt* side of the cliff.
abuse (əbyüz') v., abused, abusing. to treat cruelly or roughly. (23)
The children *abused* the puppy terribly.
address (ə dres') v., to speak to. (8)
The President *addressed* the nation on television.
aim (ām) 1. v., to point or direct a gun, weapon, etc. (8)
I *aimed* my arrow at the target, shot, and missed.
2. n., the direction of pointed a gun or weapon. (8)
Her *aim* was perfect and she hit the center of the target.
ally (al' ī) n., a person or country joined with another for a special purpose. (22)
England and France were our *allies* during World War II.
ambush (am'bush) n., the act of hiding to make a surprise attack on enemies. (5)
The general planned an *ambush* in the woods.
approach (ə prōch') n., the act of moving close; nearness. (7)
Pupils become excited at the *approach* of vacation.

approval (ǝ prü'vǝl) n., thinking well of; having a good opinion of. (23)

He showed his *approval* by smiling at us.

arms (ärmz) n. pl., weapons, guns, etc. (10)

The United States has agreed to control *arms*-making.

arouse (ǝ rouz') v., aroused, arousing. to wake up; excite. (27)

The thunder *aroused* the sleeping child.

arrangement (ǝ rānj'mǝnt) n., a plan. (16)

We made *arrangements* to meet for lunch.

aside (ǝ sīd') adv., to one side; away. (26)

The boss pushed his papers *aside* and started to talk.

at hand (I), easy to reach; nearby. (33)

You should keep a dictionary *at hand* when you write letters.

at least (I), no less than. (11)

At least twenty people were at her party.

at once (I), immediately; right now or right then. (16)

I shall answer his letter *at once*.

authority (ǝ thôr'ǝ tē) n., the right to command or act; power to make decisions. (15)

Dirk has *authority* to speak for the juniors.

avoid (ǝ void') v., to keep away from. (14)

We *avoided* large cities on our trip.

aye (ī) adv., yes. (6)

All in favor, vote *aye*.

B

ball (bôl) n., a bullet or cannon ball. (20)

Long ago soldiers carried *balls* of lead for their guns.

bank (bangk) n., a hill next to a river, lake, etc. (3)

We sat on the *bank* of the river and fished.

bear (ber) v., bore, borne, bearing. to experience or suffer. (11)

She *bore* the pain quietly.

beast (bēst) n., any animal except man, especially a four-footed animal. (6)

Camels are *beasts* that carry men in the desert.

become of (I), to happen to. (8)

What ever *became of* your friend Carrie?

bed (bed) n., the ground under a body of water. (14)

We looked for gold in the river *bed*.

beg (beg) v., begged, begging. to ask for something; ask for help. (25)

We *begged* the farmer to let us see the baby animals.

being (bē 'ing) n., a person; living creature. (21)

Every human *being* is different.

beneath (bi nēth') prep., under; below. (13)

We sat *beneath* the tree and ate our lunch.

besides (bi sīdz') adv., in addition to; also. (2)

Russell left the party because he wasn't having a good time; *besides,* he was tired.

bewildered (bi wil'dərd) adj., completely confused. (32)

John felt *bewildered* by the new school.

beyond (bi yond') prep., farther than; past. (8)

We missed the sign, and we drove *beyond* the exit.

blazing (blā 'zing) adj., glowing; flaming; bright. (6)

We sat by the *blazing* fire, toasting marshmallows.

blow (blō) n., a hard hit; attack. (9)

The boxers hit each other with many *blows.*

boast (bōst) v., to praise oneself; brag. (23)

Alberta *boasts* about her grades in school.

bold (bōld) adj., without fear; daring. (19)

The *bold* knight killed the dragon.

bounding (boun'ding) adj., jumping; leaping. (10)

The *bounding* deer went over the fence.

break off (I), to stop suddenly. (32)

They *broke off* their conversation when I entered the room.

break out (I), to speak or act suddenly. (26)

Suddenly the class *broke out* laughing.

broken English (I), English spoken poorly or with a foreign accent. (2)

Libby's mother is from Sweden and speaks *broken English.*

brush (brush) v., to touch lightly in passing. (9)

My new coat *brushed* against the dirty car.

bury (one's) knife (sword, etc.) (I), to force a weapon deep into. (32)

He *buried his knife* deep in the trunk of the tree.

bury the hatchet (I), to stop quarreling or fighting; make peace. (17)

The counsellor asked the two boys to *bury the hatchet* and become friends again.

C

cannon (kan'ən) n., a large, mounted gun. (14)
We visited the fort and looked at the *cannon.*

captive (kap'tiv) n., a prisoner. (11)
The army took many *captives* during the battle.

catch a glimpse (I), to see quickly or for a short time. (5)
I *caught a glimpse* of our house from the plane.

catch (one's) ear (I), to be heard. (17)
The noisy fight *caught the policeman's ear.*

cautiously (kô' shəs lē) adv., very carefully. (6)
Liz moved *cautiously* across the ice.

cease (sēs) v., ceased, ceasing. to stop. (8)
The children *ceased* their fighting when their mother arrived.

chant (chant) n., a kind of song. (25)
Our class learned a special *chant* to sing in church.

club (klub) n., a heavy stick used as a weapon. (12)
The farmer struck at the wild dogs with a *club.*

colors (kul'ərz) n. pl., the flag of a nation. (16)
We fly the *colors* every day on the pole in front of our school.

column (kol'əm) n., a line of persons or things in rows. (2)
We watched the *column* of soldiers march onto the field.

companion (kəm pan'yən) n., a person who is with another person. (4)
Tom and some *companions* went to a movie.

completely (kəm plēt'lē) adv., wholly; fully. (10)
The party *completely* surprised Kay.

comrade (kom'rad) n., a friend. (12)
Alex and some *comrades* went to a movie.

confess (kən fes') v., to admit one's guilt; say you have done wrong. (4)
The thief *confessed* his crime.

confused (kən fyüzd') adj., mixed up. (18)
Matt felt *confused* in the new school.

contrast (kon'trast) n., a great difference. (19)
There is a *contrast* between high school and college.

council (koun'səl) n., a meeting. (28)
The senators held a *council* to discuss the new law.

crouch (krouch) v., to stoop low with bent legs. (32)
The cat *crouched,* ready to spring on the mouse.
crow (krō) n., a large, shiny, black bird. (21)
The noise of the *crows* woke Kelly up.
crowd (kroud) n., a large group of people together. (17)
A *crowd* gathered to see the President drive through town.
current (kėr'ənt) n., a movement of water. (8)
The *current* pulled our boat down the river.

D

dare (der) v., dared, daring. to have courage; not be afraid of. (3)
The men *dared* to go out into the wild storm.
dawn (dôn) v., to grow bright or clear. (20)
Day *dawned* in the east.
deceive (di sēv') v., deceived, deceiving. to lie; trick; mislead. (4)
Lon tried to *deceive* me, but I knew he was lying.
defend (di fend') v., to protect; guard from harm. (12)
The settlers had to *defend* their homes.
delay (di lā') v., to be late; put off till a later time. (18)
We *delayed* the party for a week.
demand (di mand') v., to ask with authority; ask to be told. (3)
Ann *demanded* an answer from the two boys.
depart (di pärt') v., to leave. (1)
Frank *departed* this morning for a week's vacation.
desert (di zėrt') v., to run away from duty; leave alone. (4)
The young man *deserted* the army because he was afraid.
desperate (des'pər it) adj., careless because of lack of hope; dangerous. (32)
The prisoner made a *desperate* try to escape.
dignity (dig'n ə tē) n., an amount of honor; proud in manner. (28)
The President should always act with *dignity.*
dim (dim) adj., not clear; not bright. (14)
Our car lights were too *dim,* so Dad bought new bulbs.
disguise (dis gīz') v., disguised, disguising. to change one's clothes or appearance to look like someone else. (22)
Spies often *disguise* themselves.
dive (dīv) v., dived or dove, diving. to move out of sight suddenly. (4)
The thief *dove* down a side street.
dozen (duz'n) n., a group of twelve. (14)
Sherry bought a *dozen* eggs at the store.

draw (drô) v., drew, drawn, drawing. 1. to pull out. (2)
  She *drew* money from her wallet to pay for the tickets.
  2. to cause to come out; bring. (2)
  The clown *drew* laughter from the crowd.
duty (dü'tē) n., a responsibility; necessary job. (10)
  Parents have the *duty* to take care of their children.
dwelling (dwel'ing) n., place in which one lives; home. (21)
  They built a beautiful *dwelling* in the country.

E

ears are open (I), to listen to; pay attention to. (23)
  Velma's *ears were open* to her aunt's advice.
earshot (ir'shot) n., the distance a sound can be heard. (15)
  I was out of *earshot* and didn't hear you call.
elk (elk) n., a large deer that looks like a moose. (10)
  Lenny looked in the library for a picture of an *elk*.
emotion (i mō'shən) n., a strong feeling. (15)
  Which *emotion* do you think is stronger, love or hate?
enclose (en klōz') v., enclosed, enclosing. to shut in on all
  sides. (33)
  We *enclosed* our yard with a wooden fence.
entire (en tīr') adj., complete; total. (24)
  The *entire* class passed the test.
entrance (en'trəns) n., a door; place for entering. (9)
  I'll meet you at the *entrance* to the gym.
escort (es'kôrt) n., a guard or guide; person going with another
  for courtesy. (16)
  My sister needed an *escort* for the dinner party.
event (i vent') n., a happening. (25)
  The discovery of America was a great *event*.
expect (ek spekt') v., to think something will happen; wait
  for. (24)
  I am *expecting* to receive a letter.
exposed (ek spōzd') adj., uncovered; bare; showing. (8)
  The *exposed* film was ruined.
expression (ek spresh'ən) n., a look that shows feeling. (11)
  A smile is a happy *expression*.

F

faithful (fāth'fəl) adj., worthy of trust; doing one's duty; loyal. (8)
Jeannie's dog is her most *faithful* friend.

fall short (I), to fail to reach or do; not succeed. (32)
Our class *fell short* of its goal to raise $500.

figure (fig'yər) n., the shape of a person; person. (1)
Through the window I saw a *figure* standing on the porch.

firewater (fīr'wô tər) n., Indian phrase for liquor. (3)
Dutch settlers first gave the Indians *firewater.*

firmly (fėrm'lē) adv., tightly; solidly. (13)
We tied the boat *firmly* to the dock.

foe (fō) n., an enemy. (20)
Communists are *foes* of democracy.

fog (fog) n., a cloud near the earth. (14)
The *fog* was so bad we couldn't see the next house.

foot (fùt) n., the lowest part; bottom. (5)
We rolled on the grass to the *foot* of the hill.

force (fôrs) n., a group of soldiers, policemen, etc. (1)
Val's sister joined the police *force.*

for . . . sake (I), used with different possessive nouns to show surprise, crossness, or impatience. (5)
For heaven's *sake,* where did you come from?

fortune (fôr'chən) n., what happens to a person; fate. (9)
You cannot always control your *fortune* in life.

frame (frām) n., the body. (14)
Sean is a boy of light *frame.*

fugitive (fyü'jə tiv) n., a person who runs from danger or capture. (13)
The *fugitives* escaped the Nazis.

funeral (fyü'nər əl) adj., used at the burial of a dead person. (27)
There were many cars in the *funeral* procession.

G

gag (gag) v., gagged, gagging. to put something on the mouth to keep another from talking. (25)
The robbers tied and *gagged* the watchman.

generous (jen'ər əs) adj., willing to share with others; unselfish. (8)
Dick was amazed by the *generous* gift.

89

gesture (jes'chər) n., a movement of the hands or arms used to express feeling. (10)
He made many *gestures* during his speech.

give way (I), to move back; retreat. (7)
The enemy *gave way* before the cannon fire.

glide (glīd) v., glided, gliding. to move along smoothly and evenly. (20)
The skaters *glided* over the ice.

go to the devil (I), a rude expression meaning "go away" or "mind your own business." (16)
Ginny told her sister to *go to the devil.*

grasp (grasp) v., to hold; grab. (8)
The child *grasped* the lollipop tightly.

grave (grāv) n., a hole in the ground where a dead body is buried. (16)
Dave visited his father's *grave.*

gravely (grāv'lē) adv., seriously. (19)
He listened *gravely* to our story of the accident.

guide (gīd) 1. v., to lead or show the way. (2)
She will *guide* us to the nearest picnic area.
2. n., a person who leads or shows the way. (2)
We had a wonderful *guide* on our trip to Italy.

H

halt (hôlt) v., to stop suddenly. (2)
The policeman told the thief to *halt.*

handle (han'dl) n., the part of a thing held by the hand. (27)
Spoons, hammers, and cups have *handles.*

hand-to-hand (I), close to each other. (7)
The police and the rioters fought *hand to hand.*

happy hunting ground (I), Indian phrase for heaven; place for dead spirits. (33)
Indians buried their dead together with tools and weapons to use in the *happy hunting ground.*

harm (härm) n., hurt; damage. (5)
Gossip can cause *harm* to others.

hatchet (hach'it) n., a small ax with a short handle; tomahawk. (17)
Peg used her *hatchet* to cut firewood.

head (hed) 1. n., the upper end of a body of water. (4)
We sailed toward the *head* of the bay.
2. v., to lead; command; direct. (10)
Gracie *headed* the committee for the dance.

healing (hē'ling) n., a getting better; curing. (23)
   The Pilgrims practiced *healing* with herbs and plants.
heart is heavy (I), a feeling of sorrow; unhappiness. (23)
   Their *hearts were heavy* as they went to the funeral.
heaven (hev'ən) n., the place where God and the angels live. (32)
   "God's in His *heaven,* and all's right with the world."
hesitation (hez ə tā'shən) n., doubt; delay; uncertainty. (8)
   There was a moment's *hesitation* before Ken agreed.
Hold! (hōld) v. (imperative only), an exclamation that means stop. (14)
   The guard shouted, "*Hold!*"
hold out (I), to last; continue. (8)
   Did your food *hold out* for the whole camping trip?
horn (hôrn) n., a holder for gunpowder, often made of an animal's horn. (3)
   During the Revolutionary War, soldiers carried their gunpowder in *horns.*
hospitality (hos pə tal'ə tē) n., friendly treatment of guests. (6)
   Thank you for your *hospitality* during our visit.
human (hyü'm n) adj., people; having the form of people. (6)
   We are all *human* beings.

I

ignorant (ig'nər ənt) adj., knowing nothing. (16)
Many hearing people are *ignorant* about the deaf.
imitate (im'ə tāt) v., imitated, imitating. to copy. (19)
Children often *imitate* their parents.
individual (in də vij'ü əl) n., a person. (28)
Lenny is a fine *individual.*
inferior (in fir'ē ər) adj., less good; lower in quality. (16)
The teacher was upset because Grace's work was *inferior.*
innocent (in'ə sənt) adj., doing no wrong; not guilty. (29)
The woman said she was *innocent* of the murder.
interruption (in tə rup'shən) n., something that stops a person speaking, working, etc. (7)
I don't like *interruptions* when I'm working.
in vain (I), without success. (19)
The drowning man called *in vain* for help.
invalid (in'ə lid) n., a sick, weak person. (24)
My grandmother was an *invalid* for twenty years.
invite (in vīt') v., invited, inviting. to ask someone to come or to do something. (12)
We *invited* the whole class to dinner.

J

journey (jėr'nē) v., to travel; take a trip. (2)
My aunt and uncle *journeyed* to China last summer.
just (just) adj., honest; fair. (28)
The man offered Nels a *just* price for his bike.
justice (jus'tis) n., fair actions; correct reward or
punishment. (29)
Sometimes people must go to court to receive *justice.*

L

leap (lēp) v., leaped or leapt, leaping. to jump. (12)
The horse *leaped* over the fence.
leggings (leg'ingz) n. pl., an outer covering of cloth or leather for
the legs. (3)
Motorcycle policemen wear *leggings.*
level (lev'əl) adj., flat; even. (10)
The carpenter tore out the old floor and put in a new, *level*
floor.
likely (līk'lē) adv., probably. (14)
I shall very *likely* see you tomorrow.
litter (lit'ər) n., a framework on long poles for carrying a
person. (33)
Either men or animals may carry a *litter.*
lodge (loj) n., a small house; wigwam. (22)
Indians often made their *lodges* of bark and skins.
lose ground (I), to go backwards; retreat. (32)
Our football team *lost ground* after our quarterback
became hurt.
lost (lôst) adj., defeated; destroyed; ruined. (9)
The soldiers fought bravely but knew it was a *lost* battle.

M

madden (mad'n) v., to make or become crazy; anger. (11)
The umpire's decision *maddened* the crowd.
make way (I), to move aside so someone can go through. (26)
The crowd *made way* for the doctor.
manner (man'ər) n., the way of doing. (6)
He behaved in a strange *manner.*
mark (märk) n., a trace or sign made by one object on another. (2)
Your muddy boots left *marks* all over my clean floor!

massacre (mas'ə kər) n., the cruel, needless killing of many people. (18)
We studied the Boston *Massacre* in American history class.

meal (mēl) n., the food that people eat at one time. (6)
My family enjoyed a delicious *meal* at home.

means (mēnz) n. pl., method; way to do something. (15)
Old people have no *means* of protection against muggers.

meantime (mēn' tīm) n., the time between; same time. (7)
Do your homework; in the *meantime*, I will make dinner.

mercy (mėr'sē) n., great kindness; pity. (29)
The general showed *mercy* toward the enemy prisoners.

miracle (mir'ə kəl) n., a wonderful happening. (7)
It would be a *miracle* if the sun would stand still for an hour.

misfortune (mis fôr'chən) n., bad luck; unlucky accident. (10)
Lee had the *misfortune* to break his arm.

moment (mō' mənt) n., a minute; short time. (2)
"Wait just a *moment!*" he cried.

motion (mō' shən) v., to show what to do by moving the hand or head. (4)
He *motioned* me away.

mound (mound) n., a pile of earth or stones; small hill. (13)
We sat on a *mound* of dirt and watched the builders work.

mourner (môr'nər) n., a person who feels deep sorrow, especially at a funeral. (33)
The *mourners* wept beside the grave.

murderer (mėr'dər ər) n., a killer. (17)
The *murderer* went to jail for life.

murmur (mėr'mər) v., to complain quietly. (6)
Many members *murmured* against the club's president.

mutter (mut'ər) v., to speak in a low voice and not clearly; complain. (5)
Charles *muttered* to himself as he walked down the hall.

N

naked (nā'kid) adj., with no clothes on. (3)
The child was *naked* for the doctor's examination.

narrow (nar'ō) adj., not wide. (2)
Carrie walked carefully on the *narrow* path.

noble (nō'bəl) adj., good; worthy. (16)
Helping that poor family was a *noble* thing to do.

nod (nod) v., nodded, nodding. to move the head up and down to greet or to agree with. (24)
He didn't speak, but he *nodded* to me when he saw me.

nose to the ground (I), watching the ground carefully. (18)
We have to keep our *noses to the ground* if we want to find the lost hearing aid.

O

occasionally (ə kā'zhə nə lē) adv., now and then; sometimes. (5)
Occasionally we have hail with a summer storm.

offer (ô'fər) v., to give a promise; give. (6)
He *offered* me a job in the lunchroom.

on the other hand (I), from another side or opinion. (15)
Dad is talking about taking the family to Italy; *on the other hand*, Mom wants to visit England.

opinion (ə pin'yən) n., what one thinks; belief. (19)
Some people have the *opinion* that television is harmful to children.

opponent (ə pō'nənt) n., a person on the other side in a fight or game. (7)
Julio defeated his *opponent* in the wrestling match.

opportunity (op ər tü'nə tē) n., a good chance; favorable time. (10)
I had an *opportunity* to earn some money picking blueberries.

opposite (op' ə zit) adj., very different; exactly the other way. (4)
We live at *opposite* ends of the town.

P

pack (pak) n., a number of people, animals, or things together. (12)
They are a *pack* of liars!

paddle (pad'l) 1. v., paddled, paddling. to row a boat or canoe with a paddle. (20)
We *paddled* the canoe to an island.
2. n., a short oar with a wide blade. (20)
I dropped the *paddle*, but it floated on the water.

pale (pāl) adj., without much color; white. (9)
I was *pale* because I had been sick.

paleface (pāl'fās) n., a white person. (3)
The *palefaces* brought many diseases to the red men.

part (pärt) v., to go apart; separate. (8)
Lee was sad to *part* from his girlfriend.

parting (pär'ting) adj., given or done at the time of leaving. (10)
His *parting* words were, "See you soon!"

part with (I), to let go. (3)
We were sorry to *part with* our old car.
party (pär'tē) n., a group of people. (2)
A *party* from the Jr. National Association of the Deaf camp talked to the students.
passenger (pas'n jər) n., a traveler in a train, bus, boat, etc. who pays a fare. (5)
There were only three *passengers* on the train when it crashed.
pass for (I), to be accepted as. (22)
Ria speaks French so well that she could *pass for* a real French person.
pause (pôz) v., paused, pausing. to stop for a short time; wait. (9)
We *paused* for lunch.
pay no attention (I), to not listen to; not notice. (23)
Nick *paid no attention* to the teacher, and so he didn't understand the homework.
persuade (pər swād') v., persuaded, persuading. to get someone to do or to believe something by proof or argument. (15)
Lanny *persuaded* Gail to stop smoking.
pick . . . off (I), to kill by shooting. (32)
The rifleman *picked off* the enemy soldiers.
plain (plān) n., a flat stretch of land; prairie. (3)
The cattle moved across the *plain*.
pleasant (plez'nt) adj., nice. (2)
Our day at the beach was very *pleasant*.
pleasure (plezh'ər) n., something enjoyable; delight. (15)
Our visit to Epcot was a *pleasure*.
poor (pu̇r) adj., needing pity. (31)
The *poor* child fell and hurt himself.
powder (pou'dər) n., gunpowder. (8)
The army had kept guns and *powder* in the building that exploded.
precipice (pres'ə pis) n., a very steep cliff. (7)
In the television program, three cars went over the *precipice*.
prefer (pri fėr') v., preferred, preferring. to like better; choose rather than. (30)
I *prefer* English to math.
prejudice (prej'ə dis) n., an unfair opinion. (16)
My mom has a *prejudice* against rock music.
prepare (pri per') v., prepared, preparing. to make or get ready. (11)
We *prepared* a special dinner for Dad's birthday.

presence (prez'ns) n., appearance; being in a place. (33)
The principal's *presence* in the room made Jeannie nervous.
present (prez'nt) adj., 1. here; in this place. (27)
Everyone in the class is *present* today.
2. now. (27)
At the *present* time, I am failing science.
procession (prǝ sesh' ǝn) n., persons marching or riding
forward. (33)
Bill led the seniors in the graduation *procession*.
progress (prog'res) n., a moving forward; improvement; growth;
development. (5)
How is your *progress* in math class?
prove (prüv) v., proved, proving. to show the truth of; make
certain. (29)
The man had to *prove* that he had been far away on the
night of the murder.
Psalms (sämz) n. pl., a book of the Old Testament with 150 sacred
songs. (2)
David wrote many of the *Psalms*.
pursuit (pǝr süt') n., a following to catch; chasing. (4)
The policemen were in *pursuit* of the bank robbers.

Q

quarters (kwôr'tǝrz) n. pl., a place to live or stay. (15)
The baseball team went to winter *quarters* to practice.

R

rage (rāj) n., violent anger. (11)
Joe put his fist through a window in his *rage*.
ransom (ran'sǝm) n., the price one must pay to have a captive
freed. (30)
The kidnappers asked for a *ransom* of a million dollars.
rapidly (rap'id lē) adv., quickly. (15)
Leave the building *rapidly* during a fire drill.
rascal (ras'kǝl) n., a bad, dishonest person. (4)
That *rascal* borrowed money from Dan and never paid him
back.
rear (rir) n., the back part. (4)
The policeman walked to the *rear* of the car.

96

recognize (rek'əg nīz) v., recognized, recognizing. to remember; know. (25)

Sue hadn't seen me for three years, but she *recognized* me.

recover (ri kuv'ər) v., to become normal again after shock, illness, etc. (9)

She *recovered* quickly from the flu.

release (ri lēs') n., a letting go; setting free. (22)

The news announcer told of the *release* of the hostages.

relieved (ri lēvd') adj., free from pain, worry, etc. (31)

Mother felt *relieved* when we finally arrived home.

report (ri pôrt') n., the sound of a shot or an explosion. (4)

The *report* of a gun frightened the birds.

request (ri kwest') n., the act of asking. (16)

The teacher agreed to Mike's *request* for no homework during vacation.

revenge (ri venj') n., the harm done in return for a wrong. (11)

People who try to get *revenge* are usually not happy.

rifle (rī'fəl) n., a long gun that spins the bullet and is fired from the shoulder. (3)

Ralph cleaned his *rifle* after the hunting trip.

ring in (one's) ears (I), to stay in one's memory; remember the sound of. (6)

The yelping of the wounded dog still *rings in my ears.*

risk (risk) v., to put oneself in danger. (9)

You *risk* an accident if you drive too fast.

rustling (rus'ling) n., the soft sound of things gently rubbing together. (4)

The *rustling* of the leaves in the breeze is a pleasant summer sound.

S

sacred (sā'krid) adj., holy. (6)

He made a *sacred* promise to God.

saddle (sad'l) n., a seat for a rider on a horse's back. (1)

The cowboy jumped into the *saddle* and rode away.

salt lake (I), an ocean. (3)

Indians say the white man came to this country across the *salt lake.*

savage (sav'ij) n., a wild person. (1)

The *savages* hunted for food in the forests and streams.

scalping tuft n., a long piece of hair North American Indians left on their shaved heads. (3)

The Indian's *scalping tuft* showed he was a warrior.

scar (skär) n., a mark from a cut, burn, or sore. (11)
Josh has a small *scar* on his chin from the measles.
scatter (skat'ər) v., to separate and go in different ways; go apart. (9)
The children *scattered* to hide during the game.
scoundrel (skoun'drəl) n., a person without honor; an evil person. (5)
The *scoundrels* robbed the old woman.
seek (sēk) v., sought, seeking. to look for; try to find. (6)
The family *sought* a good camping place.
seize (sēz) v., seized, seizing. to take hold of; grasp. (12)
She *seized* his arm with fear.
senseless (sens'lis) adj., unconscious; like being asleep. (7)
A hard blow on the head knocked him *senseless*.
separate (sep'ə rāt) v., separated, separating. to go or set apart; be between. (1)
The children *separated* after school.
servant (ser'vənt) n., a person who works for another person at home. (1)
I don't have *servants* in my house.
shake (one's) head (I), to move one's head from side to side to mean no. (10)
Tony *shook his head* when I asked to borrow his bike.
sharp (shärp) adj., affecting the senses very much. (4)
The *sharp* noise made Betty jump.
sharpshooter (shärp'shü tər) n., a person who shoots a rifle very well. (29)
My cousin is a *sharpshooter* in the Marines.
shrill (shril) adj., high and sharp in sound. (23)
The *shrill* sounds of children's voices came from the gym.
shrub (shrub) n., a bush. (13)
We planted *shrubs* near the front of the house.
siege (sēj) n., the surrounding of a fort by an enemy. (15)
The *siege* of Troy in ancient Greece lasted ten years.
silent (sī'lənt) adj., quiet. (1)
The old house was *silent*.
sir (ser) n., a word of respect for a man. (15)
You are very kind, *sir.*
skin (skin) v., skinned, skinning. to scrape the skin off. (5)
He *skinned* his knee when he fell.
sly (slī) adj., tricky; able to fool; acting secretly. (4)
I don't trust Gail; she's too *sly.*
solemn (sol'əm) adj., serious. (13)
Elliott spoke to us in a *solemn* voice about his sister's illness.

spring (spring) 1. v., sprang, sprung, springing. to jump; leap. (1)
Santa *sprang* to his sleigh.
2. n., a flow (movement) of water coming from the ground. (12)
We found a *spring* of cool, clear water in the woods.

spy (spī) n., a person sent by one government to get secret information in another country. (3)
Major André was a British *spy* during the Revolutionary War.

squaw (skwô) n., a North American Indian woman or wife. (24)
The *squaw* did the gardening while her husband was hunting.

stagger (stag'ər) v., to move unsteadily from weakness, a heavy load, etc. (24)
The old man *staggered* across the room.

stake (stāk) n., a post for tying and then burning someone to death. (25)
The English burned Joan of Arc at the *stake*.

stammer (stam'ər) v., to hesitate in speaking; repeat the same sound. (16)
The child *stammered* with fear when he tried to answer.

stand by (I), to stand beside or near. (17)
Dick *stood by* and watched the two boys fight.

stare (ster) v., stared, staring. to look at for a long time. (11)
The boys *stared* at the cute new girl in the class.

start (stärt) v., to give a sudden movement from surprise or fright. (21)
The deer *started*, and then he ran.

steady (sted'ē) v., steadied, steadying. to keep calm or firm. (32)
The woman tried to *steady* her nerves after the accident.

steal (stēl) v., stole, stolen, stealing. to move secretly or quietly. (9)
Ray *stole* out of the house before anyone else was awake.

steel (stēl) n., a hard, strong metal; something made from this metal. (14)
Most tools are made of *steel*.

steep (stēp) adj., almost straight up and down. (10)
We climbed the *steep* mountain all day.

stoop (stüp) v., to bend forward. (13)
The tall man *stooped* to get through the low doorway.

strength (strengkth) n., power. (15)
Young men often lift weights to increase their *strength*.

strike (strīk) v., struck, striking. to hit. (4)
Al *struck* Mike during the fight.

suffering (suf'ər ing) n., pain or misery. (24)

Hunger in the world causes much *suffering*.

sullen (sul'ən) adj., silent because of anger or bad temper. (1)

The *sullen* child refused to obey his mother.

support (sə pôrt') v., to assist; supply what one needs. (16)

The Navy *supported* the Marines during the battle.

surrender (sə ren'dər) n., the act of giving up or yielding to another. (15)

The *surrender* of the fort was necessary.

surround (sə round') v., to shut in on all sides; encircle. (9)

The soldiers *surrounded* the village.

suspiciously (sə spish'əs lē) adv., doubtfully; feeling mistrust. (2)

She looked at me *suspiciously* when I offered to help.

sweep (swēp) v., swept, sweeping. to move quickly. (5)

The wind *swept* my hat from my head and down the street.

swift (swift) adj., moving at great speed; quick. (4)

Ann is a *swift* runner and should win the race.

T

tap (tap) n., a light touch or noise. (20)

I felt a *tap* on my shoulder.

tender (ten'dər) adj., kind; loving; gentle. (22)

The nurse showed her patients *tender* care.

the rest (I), what is left; others. (1)

She stayed at home while *the rest* of us went to the party.

thicket (thik'it) n., a number of bushes growing close together. (13)

Harmon crawled into the *thicket* and hid.

threaten (thret'n) v., to say one will hurt or punish another person. (14)

The farmer *threatened* to shoot any dog that killed his sheep.

throw (one) off (I), to mislead; confuse; fool. (20)

The fox doubled back to *throw the dog off* his trail.

thrust (thrust) n., a push with force; sudden, sharp attack. (12)

The knight killed his enemy with a *thrust* of his sword.

timid (tim'id) adj., shy; easily frightened. (17)

Deer are *timid* animals.

tomahawk (tom' ə hôk) n., a light ax Indians used as a weapon and a tool. (1)

Sandy enjoyed seeing the *tomahawks* at the museum.

tortoise (tôr'təs) n., a kind of turtle. (22)

We watched the *tortoise* move slowly across the driveway.

torture (tôr'chər) n., the act of causing very severe pain. (25)
Many Jews suffered *torture* during World War II.
trace (trās) n., a mark or sign. (29)
We saw *traces* of rabbits on the snow.
traitor (trā'tər) n., a person who is unfaithful to his country, ruler, friend, etc. (30)
A person who sells his country's secrets is a *traitor.*
trembling (trem'bling) adj., shaking. (11)
Mother comforted the *trembling* child.
trigger (trig' ər) n., the small lever that one pulls to fire a gun. (4)
Draw the *trigger* slowly and carefully.
triumph (trī'umf) n., victory; success. (7)
Our team returned in *triumph* from the tournament.
truce (trüs) n., a temporary peace. (31)
The two armies agreed to a *truce.*
trunk (trungk) n., the main part of a tree. (8)
Evie hid behind the *trunk* of a tree while the other children looked for her.
turn . . . against (I), to become angry with; make another angry. (22)
Sue has *turned* Carol *against* Rae.

U

unconscious (un kon'shəs) adj., not awake; not able to know what is happening. (17)
He was *unconscious* during the operation.
unfortunate (un fôr'chə nit) adj., not lucky. (16)
She is an *unfortunate* person, and I feel sorry for her.
utter (ut' ər) v., to speak; say. (12)
He *uttered* a cry of pain.

V

victim (vik'təm) n., a person or animal who suffers or dies. (2)
The ambulance arrived to help the *victims* of the accident.
villain (vil'ən) n., a very bad person. (11)
The *villain* stole money and blamed his friend.
volley (vol'ē) n., a shower of stones, bullets, arrows, etc. (20)
The police fired a *volley* of shots at the robbers.

W

weeping (wē'ping) adj., crying. (17)
  Judith tried to comfort the *weeping* child.
whirlpool (hwėrl'pül) n., a place where the water whirls round and round violently. (5)
  Lee watched the tiny *whirlpool* in the bathtub drain.
whoop (hüp) n., a loud shout. (9)
  Chuck gave a *whoop* of joy when he opened his gift.
wicked (wik'id) adj., bad; evil. (25)
  He spoke *wicked* words, and people were afraid.
wigwam (wig'wom) n., an Indian hut made of bark or skins laid over a frame of poles. (11)
  Some Indians of the Northeast lived in *wigwams*.
wilderness (wil'dər nis) n., a wild place with no people living in it. (1)
  The settlers traveled across the mountains into the *wilderness* of Kentucky.
wisdom (wiz'dəm) n., knowledge; being wise. (27)
  Wisdom comes only after much experience.
worship (wėr'ship) v., to think of as wonderful. (3)
  Some people *worship* money.